DESTINY OF LIFE

Tom Pim

Destiny of Life

copyright © Tom Pim 2001

ISBN 1 903607 16 7

2nd edition

This work is a novel and any similarity to actual persons is purely coincidental.

The ship shown on the cover is *Commodore Ship Empire Archer* which Tom Pim sailed in on his second voyage to Russia.

Typesetting and production by

Able Publishing
13 Station Road
Knebworth
Hertfordshire SG3 6AP

Tel: 01438 812320 / 814316
Fax: 01438 815232

www.ablepublishing.co.uk
email: fp@ablepublishing.co.uk

Destiny of Life

It soon became obvious that the Condor had fulfilled its role when, as night fell, the first torpedo struck. It was the American *S.S. Dallas* that had been so kind to us in Iceland that was hit.

In one mighty roar she blew. The whole night seemed to come alight. The sea heaved and the waves flung themselves into the air. Then there was complete darkness, as a searing hot wave of air rushed over *The Usworth*.

The *S.S. Dallas* had vanished.

The escort destroyers raced around, laying patterns of depth charges; but it soon became obvious there was more than one U-boat in this attack.

About The Author

Tom retired from the sea where he once worked as Chief Purser, for Union Castle-Clanline. He spent most of his sea time in Harrison Line Liverpool. He now lives in a Cotswold Village, Worcestershire, with his wife Bette, who is a poet, and has had her work published many times in anthologies. Together their main interest is watching polo at Cirencester Park and Beaufort Polo Clubs. They enjoy the peacefully beautiful Cotswold countryside.

This is the story of a young man's experiences during World War Two. His childhood in an orphanage, in conditions which would be unthinkable today. However, the very harsh regime prepares him for the War, the bombings and sinkings, and the many cruel deaths he witnessed. In the Battle of the Atlantic, O'Dell helps rescue the troops. He then goes on to face the horrific experiences of the Russian Convoy run, before serving in North Africa and Sicily.

*This book is dedicated to all members
of the Merchant Navies, 1939 - 1945
Let us not forget those who did not survive,
Their graves, the cruel seas.*

ARCTIC CONVOYS

It's 1942 and I am just a boy, going off to sea.
Straight from Naval School I went, to help the Nazi flee.
Fifteen and a half I was, with all my life ahead,
to the horrors of arctic war, and all the many dead.
On Russian Convoys so many gave their lives
to help the poor and needy, so that they could survive.
Seeing my shipmates frozen dead is terrible to behold,
I saw a youth bend to help a mate, the sea washed over cold
and eternally froze them solid in that stance,
like statutes in ice, in the split second of a glance.
One dreadful day in the freezing icy blasts
the U boats came and sank us – extremely fast.
Someone watched over me? For I was quickly snatched
from those icy seas around us, with speed you couldn't match,
frozen and wounded from the violent explosions.
My sixteenth birthday in hospital, I had no notion
that I almost lost my legs! Those clever doctors saved
or I would be a cripple if my legs I gave.
When I fully recovered to sail those seas twice more
I was lucky not to be torpedoed as I was before.
Years later in 1986, a commemorative medal was struck.
Russian Convoy Survivors received it, to remind us of our luck,
as though we could ever forget all the horrors we endured,
and just hope and pray that peace really is secured.
So, when you see the 'White Berets' marching on parade,
just remember who they are – and all the lives they gave.

Bette Pim

Chapter One

He approached the large ornate wrought iron gates of the Russian Consulate.

Slowly, he told himself, it's not too late to turn back. But he knew in his heart he would go through with it.

When the Russian Embassy in London had sent that letter eighteen months ago to inquire if he was indeed ex-Boy Seaman Thomas Samuel O'Dell R268793, Russian Convoy Survivor *H.M.S. Usworth* 1942-43, if so would he be kind enough to forward his seafaring papers, he was more than surprised; but it appeared that the Russians, after all these years, wanted to present him with a medal.

He and his wife Betty had talked long and hard about the letter.

Would it re-open all those nightmares, those horrors that had taken years to fade, but were still buried in his subconscious?

On the other hand it was marvellous news that at last those Russian convoys would receive recognition.

People had tried so hard over the years to get some form of recognition from Prime Ministers, from Attlee to Thatcher, but the answer had always been the same:

'The Lords of the Admiralty consider the Atlantic Star sufficient.'

This was a ludicrous claim, like saying that the Pacific Star covered Burma too.

He got frustrated and angry with these answers over the years, and had tried to get newspapers and radio and television studios interested, but with no joy.

It seemed that no-one wanted to know.

Now, at last, Russia began to remember. It was a political move, of course; 'Gorby Glasnost' carried on by the new Russian leader, but might it not awake the British Government to give a well-earned recognition to the men on those horrendous convoys of long ago?

Even a rosette on the Atlantic Star medal, similar to that given to the 8th Army on the Africa Star, would be sufficient.

Now he reached the gates of the Russian Embassy and rang the bell.

They were opened by a smiling Russian sailor, who beckoned him in, and took him to the main door of the Consulate, which opened as they approached.

At this he smiled to himself. Obviously television surveillance was in operation.

He was met at the door by a smartly dressed Russian who introduced herself as one of the Consul's assistants. She told him her name was Anna Dobrinka.

He presented his letter, and the invitation. She read them and assured him, smilingly, that it was the Russian people's pleasure to welcome him. She also told him that he was the youngest survivor of the Russian Convoys that they had managed to contact so far.

She guided him to the Reception Room, and introduced him to the consul Gregor Koroski, who gave him a warm smile and a firm handshake.

'Welcome!' he said, and escorted him round the room, introducing him to members of his Staff and to other veterans of the Convoys who were present.

What a cross-section of personnel it was, from the Royal Navy, the Merchant Navy, the Royal Naval Reserve, the Royal Air Force and the Army. There were even a couple like himself—known as T124X, and Army lads, the D.E.M.S., and what the Merchant Navy would have done without these was awful to contemplate.

When a sailor appeared at his side with a tray of drinks of all sorts, vodka, gin and whisky, he'd declined with thanks. He would prefer a soft drink, please, and they brought him a glass of iced orange juice which he found refreshing as well as enjoyable.

As he sipped his drink slowly he listened to the seafarers re-living their part in the Convoys. He felt time had lent enchantment to their memories.

Or was it perhaps a way of blocking out the true horrors of those voyages long ago?

When their Russian hosts were satisfied that everyone had arrived that were expected, the guests were taken into an adjoining room and lined up to hear the speech.

The Consul, on behalf of the Russian people, thanked them for their help against the filthy. Fascist hordes in Russia in their hour of great need. He then moved along the lines, pinning on the medals, then giving each seafarer a big hug, and a kiss on both cheeks.

He had to smile to himself.

A hug from a Russian Bear? Who would have thought that possible in the 1940s? Certainly not the lads on *H.M.S. Usworth*!

As had obviously been pre-arranged, one of the survivors stepped forward, and on their behalf thanked the Consul, his Staff, and the Russian people for the wonderful reception and the recognition the medal implied.

Recognition of the time when Russia and Britain had stood side by side, shoulder to shoulder against the might of Fascist Germany.

He reminded each one of us that the Germany of today still held the same people, regardless of N.A.T.O. Now the Wall had fallen we must be forever on our guard.

The speeches and presentations over, the vodka appeared again. Drinks forward!

While he was chatting with some of the veterans, he found some who had been on the same convoys as himself, though not the same ships.

The seafarer who had spoken on their behalf introduced himself as the Chairman of the Anglo-Russian Friendship Society. Although this man had sailed to Russia in 1944 on a Battle wagon escort, sailing from Lock Ewe to Murmansk and back, he had never set a foot ashore in Russia.

As usual war talk started to make him feel nervous and uptight, and although he still had more than three hours to wait for his train home, he decided to leave as soon as it was reasonable to do so.

Eventually, when he made his excuses to leave, the lady who'd greeted him on arrival appeared from somewhere to escort him to the door. There she thanked him sincerely again for his help against the Fascist hordes that had ravished her country.

Even after all the intervening years he could still detect the bitterness and enmity in her voice. He reckoned she was only in her thirties, yet she obviously hated Germany for what it had done to her beloved Motherland.

He thanked her for her kindness and courtesy.

'I am so very proud to receive the medal,' he told her.

'Please visit the Embassy any time,' she answered. 'Nothing is too good for Russia's friends who proved their worth during those terrible dark days so long ago.'

Outside the Consulate gates he looked at his watch. There were nearly three hours to go before his train went. He'd take a walk around.

Not having been in Liverpool for eight years or so, he'd time to walk to Pier Road to look at the river, maybe even go into the new Maritime Museum. He'd heard that it was excellent.

But when he got to the Pier Head he was amazed at the changes there. He walked up to what looked like an observation block.

He sat down. Goodness, what a difference!

Everywhere he looked only two things seemed constant: the river itself and the ferries. Otherwise nothing was how he remembered it. The landing stage and the river were empty: the famous Mersey empty; he could hardly believe it. Everything was so desolate and run down.

As he tucked his scarf tighter round his throat as a protection against the cold breeze coming off the river he couldn't help but recall it as he remembered it, so full of life and movement. Then there were ships of every shape and size: Clan, Harrison, Elder Dempster Booth, Palm Line, all waiting for berths.

And tankers too, moving up river to Eastham.

The larger passenger ships, Cunard C.P.R. and Union Castle, tying up at the landing stage. Some voyages just starting, others at the end of their cruise. Round them tugs would be fussing, blowing their little shrill whistles, the toot-toots mingling with the loud harsh horns of the deep sea vessels.

With a start he brought himself back to reality, and thought again of the reception he'd just left, and the bitterness in the voice of Anna Dobrinka.

He sighed. In his thirty-five years at sea he had heard the same bitterness from many of his friends; South African Boers, Irish, West Indians, Canadians and even the Welsh.

Chapter Two

They all somehow felt the English had done them a wrong over the years. It's a funny old world, he thought, full of love but of hate too.

His thoughts once more drifted back to the past, back to Russia.

Nothing could have been more ironic than the reason the Russian Convoys came into being.

Stalin deeply distrusted the West, but realised without their help he could lose the war. The Russians had the courage, pride and moral fibre, what they lacked was equipment. The Allies, on the other hand, were well aware that if Russia lost, their fight against Germany and Japan would last twice as long, and what was more important it would cost hundreds of thousands more lives. Hence the Russian Convoys were organised in mutual distrust, but logically this was unavoidable.

They sentenced the Allied seamen to a living hell in those cold, oh so cold, cruel seas; but the high price in blood was to be hidden from the British people until the war was over.

He knew he would never forget that terrible period of his life. True those awful nightmares had faded with time, but every now and then they returned to give him sleepless nights.

His wife used to say, when they were first married, that he either cried or fought in his sleep every night. But over the years her compassion and understanding calmed him down.

He now, thank God, slept well every night.

There have been bitter years when he had sincerely believed there was no God, especially after his experiences on the Russian run.

He had felt so proud the day he had joined the *H.M.S. Usworth* to be back in bellbottoms and tunic, and as he climbed her gangway for the first time, turning aft to salute, he thought his heart would burst with joy, to be back in uniform, to be on a real Navy ship.

Oh how young, daft and excited he had been, and careful to hide his feelings when he reported to the P.O. of the deck. The first thing the P.O. said was, 'Hand over your white cap, son: no more white caps until the war is over. Blue caps only.'

It appeared that the powers that be thought the Germans could see the white flashes from the air when flying over the ship.

They came up with some funny ideas during the war: some real beauties, like painting out names of railway stations and names at crossroads. Did they really believe that if Jerry did arrive he would be too stupid to look into a churchyard to discover where he was?

As he handed over his white cap, he thought of the boys at the Naval Training School he had left fifteen months ago. Had they handed in their white caps? What would they think if they could see him joining the *H.M.S. Usworth* and being in the T124X?

The week before, on joining the T124X, he had been given orders to proceed to. Cardiff to join *The Usworth* when his leave was finished. He had joined his draft at the depot, Bute Dock.

The ship had been in dry dock, fitting out for the Russian run.

H.M.S. Usworth was a converted cargo/passenger liner, owned by the Tyne Steamship Company, taken over by the Government for the duration of the war. She had been completely gutted out; all accommodation, including between decks, had been covered with plywood, three inches from all bulkheads, with sawdust poured between to help insulate the ship from the severe cold Arctic waters. All steam pipes and any water taps on deck received the same treatment.

The first duties of the dock watch, as the ship left dry-dock, was to clear up the mess left by joiners, carpenters and dockers, and it was a mess! To say the deck watch was not very happy would be an understatement. They were full of loud groans and bitching. They had no conception at that period just how grateful they were to become, in the next two months, for all the work done by the workers In Cardiff dry dock.

The Usworth had been converted to a Hospital/Rescue ship. The Port side accommodation not only became a hospital but all medical staff, doctors, male nurses, were housed there. On her Starboard Side lived extra Deck and Engineer Officers. There was an extra galley, with catering staff housed at the far end.

The ship was bristling with guns. most of them anti-aircraft. Aft of the Port and Starboard wings of the bridge there were gun emplacements, double strength, which were in theory to protect those on the bridge.

14

The ship's holds had also been put to use. Number I held extra gunners and extra crew members; Number II was fitted out and prepared for survivors, while the aft hold was fitted out as a repair shop, with housing for blacksmiths, welders and electricians.

O'Dell was ordered to report to the C.P.O.

Emberton, the 'Chief Bunts.'

On reporting to him, Bunts asked, 'First trip son?'

'No sir, second trip. Just finished an eleven month voyage.'

'Bunts looked at him. 'How old are you?'.

I'm sixteen years old sir.'

Bunts sighed, they were getting younger all the time. 'Report to Leading Seaman Brown once you have stowed your gear,' he ordered.

Accommodation had been newly built between the engine-room skylights and of the bridge on the Boat deck for the Signal Section.

Stowing his gear in the bunk space allotted to him, he discovered the Signal Section comprised Chief Petty Officer Emberton ('BUNTS'), Leading Hand Brown, four A.B. Ratings (Signals) and, including himself, four Boy Seamen (Signals).

This information was passed to him by another Boy Seaman, already in the Signal Section. who had introduced himself as 'Miles Kemp.' It appeared that he'd already been on board a week.

Miles could not control his astonishment when he found out that this was not O'Dell's first voyage.

'You mean you already have a trip under your belt?'

'Sure' he replied. 'An eleven month voyage.' And when he added it had been in the Merchant Navy and not Royal Navy, Miles' face was a picture.

'I'll explain later,' he promised.

A noise at the door made them both turn round. He couldn't believe his eyes, but stood to attention and just stared.

'OK Titch, relax,' said Leading Hand Brown. 'I wondered if it was the same O'Dell when I saw the draft list. I guess you are not called Titch now. You have grown.'

As Brown stepped forward, putting out his hand, O'Dell remembered how he had grasped it, and Brown had smiled.

'Well,' he said, 'At least I shall know someone this voyage.' Then turning to B.S. Kemp he said, 'We were both in the same Naval

15

Training School, although I was two years ahead of O'Dell.' Then, turning again he said, 'If I remember rightly you were known even then for your fast Morse, O'Dell. Are you still as fast?'

O'Dell blushed, and stammered. Brown had been in his dormitory Killock in the Naval School, and he was finding it hard to adjust. Here was a man he'd had to stand to attention for whenever he had spoken to him, for at least two years.

Now, trying to hold a conversation with Brown, he found it extremely hard going; Brown had sensed how he felt and tried to put him at ease.

'If I remember alright, last time we spoke was during an air raid practice, right O'Dell?' He'd nodded his head.

'I thought they should have let us sleep, didn't You?' asked Brown. He remembered then, that it had been L.S. Brown on the last night in the Naval School, who would have left; is they all did that were going to sea. It was traditional that spot on 0930 hours those leaving for sea marched through the gates, the band playing, and the O.O.D. saluting them.

Brown would not have known what happened to him that awful morning, O'Dell thought. A wave of rage washed over him as that awful memory came back. He could see and hear Lt. Comdr. Yearly as if it were only yesterday.

He had not been aware at that time that Brown did know what had happened: a letter from one of the boys in his dormitory had seen to that.

Now he heard Brown saying, 'Come on O'Dell.

I will take you up to the bridge and show you your duties.'

He followed him out of the accommodation, up the outer companionway to the bridge.

On entering they found the Navigating Officer and Bunts already there. Brown saluted. 'New Boy seaman O'Dell, Sir' he reported.

The Navigating Officer had looked at him. Then turning to Bunts he said, 'God they are sending children now!'

Bunts replied 'I thought the same myself Sir, when he reported on board.'

The Navigator looked at him.

'How old O'Dell?'

He sprang to attention. 'Sixteen years, Sir.'

Navigator sighed. 'There's no need for all that spit and polish on the bridge, O'Dell. And don't keep springing to attention when someone speaks to you. Keep all that for Inspections and muster, unless of course it's the Captain speaking. We have enough trouble trying to stop Brown, with his parade ground performance, without someone else starting.'

Then obviously a thought crossed his mind. 'You're not from the same Naval School, are you?'

'Yes Sir,' O'Dell replied.

'Oh my God!' said the Navigator, and. walked off the bridge into the chart room. He looked across at Brown who was looking bashful, embarrassed even.

'They think the Naval School taught us too much parade marching and saluting,' he explained, 'but they admit we are the best trained signallers.'

Brown proceeded to take him around the bridge, chart house and emergency room, then gave him his duty roster. He would be on the same watch as Brown. His main duties would be moving Morse lamps, as required; pulling out correct signal flags as required from their pigeon holes; blow the bugle if required, and at all times to be available to carry messages for any officer on the bridge.

Returning to their accommodation, Brown introduced him to the rest of the Signal Section, the ratings shook his hand, and welcomed him aboard.

The three Boy Seamen (Signals) bombarded him with questions as to where he'd sailed on his eleven month voyage. Had he seen action? How long had he been in the Merchant Navy then, and Royal Navy now? A host of questions flew thick and fast. He'd explained he was now T124X. What was that, they wanted to know?

'It's when you join the Royal Navy, accept Royal Navy uniforms and discipline but get paid Merchant Navy wages.'

'Yes!' shouted one of the ratings. 'He gets paid nearly as much as we men ratings.'

'That's true,' he replied. 'But I have to buy all my own heavy weather gear. Also if we are sunk my wages stop there and then, even if I am away from the United Kingdom for a year. My wages do not start again until I sign on my next ship, whereas if you're sunk your wages continue to be paid.'

'That's true,' conceded the Rating.

'Why did you want to join the T124X?' asked Miles.

'Because I felt my training in the Naval School was wasted in the Merchant Navy.'

'Why didn't you stay in the Naval School and go to sea from there, like Leading Hand Brown?' asked another Boy Seaman. This was a question he had prepared himself for.

'I wanted to go to sea as soon as possible. If I'd stayed at the Naval School I wouldn't have been allowed at sea until I was at least seventeen years old.'

That night Brown had told Bunts about him, and what had happened to him the day Brown had left.

'Poor sod,' said Bunts.

'I only hope he doesn't blame me,' Brown said. 'I can assure you, C.P.O., when I told the P.O. on watch what O'Dell had said, I never meant it as a report. just a casual remark. I certainly never thought it would lead to what transpired. I feel guilty in a way. It was such an innocent remark that I never gave it a thought afterwards. Do you think I should let O'Dell be aware I know what happened, Bunts?'

'Never, never let on you know, Brown.'

Although he was the youngest Boy Seaman (Signals), since he was the only one with sea time Bunts put him in charge of the other three, under Leading Hand Brown.

Next morning all hands were ordered to muster aft at 1030 hours.

At first it appeared that the O.O.D. was going to muster all T124X separately, but a message from the Jimmy No: I soon put paid to that. So all the blacksmiths, electricians, extra catering staff, medical staff and extra stokehold ratings mustered with R.N.

The appearance of the Captain, spot on 1030 hours, gave us the reason why he'd only joined the ship late the night before.

He was Captain W. Robertson R.N.R.

After reading out the 'ARTICLES OF WAR' the Captain asked the Jimmy to stand the ship's company at ease. This done, he then explained exactly what the duties of the H. M. S. Usworth were, and what he expected from every member of the ship's company. Her job was to be the 'Tail end Charlie' in every convoy she sailed in. Her main function was to pick up survivors, getting those injured to the ship's hospital, or to No. 3 hold, which had been converted to house two hundred survivors. She was also a floating repair ship, to help repair any damage done by the enemy to other ships, that was feasible.

'The job is hard, and extremely dangerous,' the Captain continued, 'but I'm sure everyone knows how important it is to work together as a team: as one unit at all times.'

'We are,' he concluded, 'a mixed bunch, R.N., R.N.R., R.N.V.R. and last but not least T124X. But from this moment we are ALL R.N. and will serve as such.'

Bringing himself to attention, he saluted, with the words, 'Gentlemen, I salute you.'

Then turning to the Jimmy, Lt. Comdr. Charlton, R.N., he said, 'Carry on, Number One.'

On being dismissed, the whole ship was alive with an excited buzz at the Captain's salute.

It was wise old Bunts that summed it up. He said, 'All the Captain's done is win everyone to his side; at the same time he's shown that he is a real gentleman.'

That night, the last of shore leave, the Boy Seamen were allowed ashore up to 2100 hours, but they decided to stay onboard and turn in early, after having a good yarn. At their request O'Dell told them more about his first trip, but he never mentioned what had happened off Tobruk. He felt they were not ready for that, any more than he had been at the time.

He'd been awakened by the return of the Ratings, who were well-worse for drink, and as he listened it became obvious that the Ratings had been in a fight, but not with another ship's crew, but with some of the deck crew. He heard one of the Ratings voicing his disgust that some of the crew had gone to the rescue of what he called, 'the ginger headed bastard.'

Eventually Bunts called for lights out, and all talking ceased.

As he drifted off to sleep O'Dell wondered what the ginger headed sailor had done. Somehow he felt sure the signal Rating had been referring to the Scot redhead who had been in the same draft as himself.

It had been noticeable that even the P.O.'s had treated the big Scotsman with slightly different attitude from the rest of the draft. It was certainly not because of his size or build, P.O.'s chewed up ratings of all sizes and then spat them out. The last thought, as sleep claimed him, was 'I'll try to find out more tomorrow.'

The next morning at 0900 hours *H.M.S. Usworth* slipped her moorings and swung her bow out to the middle of the dock, and proceeded to enter the centre lock, then out to sea.

He had been on the bridge most of the time, thrilled as they had slowly eased past ship after ship, Bunt's whistle filling the morning air as they saluted, and were saluted in return, their lovely new white ensign dipping up and down.

This was it, he had told himself, utter happiness, sheer joy.

At last he was under the white ensign; at last he could serve his country. Oh the Ignorance of youth. Thank goodness one can never read the future.

The next three days were hard, damned hard work, in the bay of Milford Haven.

They had, apart from sea trials, a real sea shakedown, and watch keeping ceased as the whole ship's crew practices over and over again every kind of emergency, from going alongside a ship on fire and sinking and rescuing survivors, to target practice, the targets sometimes being towed by tugs, other times by an old Lysander flying over. In fact every emergency they could be called on to face.

The Captain soon lost his popularity as he drove the officers and crew, over and over again. After three days, although the Captain was not fully satisfied. *The Usworth* was ordered to join the convoy that had been forming off Milford Haven. Much to the joy of the whole ship's company, it appeared that the pilot of the Lysander had twice signalled, 'You are supposed to hit the tow, NOT repeat NOT me.'

When informed he would not be required for target practice the next day, the pilot had signalled, 'Thank God. Hope you frighten the Jerries as much as you have me.'

The Captain was not amused.

The Usworth joined the convoy late in the afternoon. The Navy had at last got the Merchant ships in their allotted places, with much chivvying and chasing.

The Commodore. Rear Admiral Churms, who had been brought out of retirement, signalled 'Welcome. Hope you won't be needed on voyage.'

The Captain in charge of the escort also came alongside once *Usworth* was in position to 'welcome' her, and informed our Captain that he would see him when the convoy reached Iceland, to discuss details relating to the next part of the voyage to Russia.

At 1700 hours, the Commodore ordered the convoy to proceed and added, 'GOOD LUCK.'

Slowly the convoy moved out to the deep sea.

By 1900 hours *The Usworth* was in her allotted position as Tail End Charlie. After three hectic days of shake-down, those off duty just collapsed into their bunks, or hammocks, while the others stood their watch, raw-eyed and tired even before the voyage had begun.

Dawn broke, the sea was choppy and angry, and the West Coast of Ireland was coming up on the starboard side.

O'Dell and Brown had been relieved at 0800 hours and were having their cocoa and porridge when Bunts came in.

'Sorry, but you two will have to do an extra watch each. One now, one following.'

It appeared three of the Boy Seamen and two of the Signal Ratings had succumbed to sea sickness; two of the boys were really bad.

Brown suggested we tossed for it, but Bunts said, 'You first O'Dell, Brown you follow and take charge while I get my head down. I will take next watch with O'Dell.'

Brown went from the Mess to the signal quarters. The boy seamen were ill and wanted to die. Remembering how ill he had been on his first trip, he could sympathise and feel for them! The only comfort he could give was that he had felt the same, and although they didn't believe it now, the sickness would pass.

Eventually they arrived off Iceland, with only a couple of hiccups.

First, off the West Coast of Ireland they had sailed past some Irish fishing boats. The Jimmy Number 1 had muttered a small curse, and said to the navigator, 'Just our luck! The Germans will have all the details of this convoy by nightfall.'

Later O'Dell asked Brown what the Jimmy had meant, and Brown explained that the Southern Irish fishing fleets were thought to inform German Consuls the details of every convoy they saw, as they hated the British.

Bunts overheard this exchange and said, 'Don't forget, Brown, we have some in our forces fighting the Germans too.'

As Bunts moved away, Brown said in a low voice, 'Not as many as the Germans have on their side. It's even alleged that they actually re-fuel U-boats in various harbours.'

O'Dell remembered Alexandria, and knew what Brown meant.

The second hiccup came when one of the merchant ships had engine trouble leading to a fire in her engine room. *Usworth* had been ordered to assist her, but the ship had managed to put out the fire. However she signalled she could only do five knots now and was leaving the convoy. So *Usworth* was ordered to escort the ship, which was one of Hugh Robert's Fleet Newcastle-on-Tyne, to the safety of the North Irish Coast and then to rejoin the convoy.

On arrival off Iceland at the port of Reykjavik the merchant ships anchored while the R.N. ships patrolled up and down like shepherds watching their flock.

Two days later the signal went out for all Merchant Navy Captains and their Radio Operators to proceed ashore for last minute instructions before heading for Archangel and Murmansk.

Usworth was ordered to supply duty boats and to collect the Captains and their Radio Operators from each Merchant ship.

O'Dell managed to get on one of the duty boats as they awaited at the bottom of each Merchant man, they were able to exchange news and gossip with the crews.

The American Merchant ship, *S. S. Dallas*, was kind enough to lower a box full of goodies: sweets, chocolate, fur-lined gloves, hats, and even a case of Coca Cola. The boat's crew thought Christmas had come early.

After returning all the merchant personnel to the ships, they shared the box of goodies among themselves before heading back to their own ship.

O'Dell got himself a smashing pair of fur-lined gloves, which were to prove invaluable during the voyage ahead.

In the meantime the convoy had been joined by another ten ships which had come up from Canada. Three were Greek, two American, two Canadian and three British, plus one of their escorts, a Polish destroyer. The other part of their escort returned whence they had come.

Once the new arrivals had settled in their allotted positions the Commodore signalled convoy to proceed. They slowly moved out, the R.N. ships already ahead, fanning out to port and starboard, with *The Usworth* way at the stern.

Two mornings out of Iceland they had their first snow storm, and the sea became wild, grey, and very rough. The temperature dropped to ten degrees below, and it made the Mess no happier to hear Bunts telling one of the Ratings, 'This is nothing. Last time I was in Russia at Murmansk in 1920 it was forty degrees below at times.'

They just could not imagine anywhere as cold as that and it was generally agreed that Bunts, like all old timers, was letting his imagination run away.

Oh what a lot they had to learn!

The next three weeks would see them grow from young boys to old men; at least those who survived would age rapidly.

They had just got into the daily routine, with an extra practice or two, when they lost their first ship, *S.S. Felling*.

She had been dropping behind, unable to maintain ten knots full time. She had been chased up back into position a few times by the escorts; the Commodore had even sent a couple of messages by lamp for her to hold her position.

The ship was old, and obviously should have been in a slower convoy.

It was just after 2200 hours when the first torpedo struck the Felling right aft, blowing rudder and steering gear completely off. The second one got her amidships, and the old *S.S. Felling* started to die.

The Usworth was ordered to go to her aid, and to pick up survivors without getting in the escort's way, who were now, it seemed to the uninitiated, throwing depth charges all over the place. But in truth they were laying them out in perfect pattern.

The Captain took over the bridge, and in no time brought *The Usworth* astern of the crippled, sinking ship. All hands not on watch were turned to, some manning the side netting, others fire hoses, while the hospital staff prepared for its first casualties.

A lamp started to blink from the *Felling.* She told *Usworth* she had launched two lifeboats, and reminded *Usworth* not to get any closer as she was loaded with ammunition and would blow up at any minute.

Officer of the Watch ordered Bunts to acknowledge.

O'Dell heard someone on the bridge voice what they were all thinking: that someone on the *S.S. Felling* had a lot of guts.

The Jimmy barked out, 'No talking on the bridge,' followed by Bunts: 'Keep those signallers quiet!'

The Captain went on the Tannoy to order everyone to keep their eyes peeled for torpedoes, U-boats surfacing and survivors, in that order.

One of the escorts came racing up *The Usworth's* port side, and on the hailer informed *Usworth* she had just passed a lifeboat from *S.S. Felling*.

Once again the Captain turned *The Usworth* and started to the area from which the escort had come; half an hour later the lifeboat was spotted. *The Usworth* slowed down–as slow as she dared. The Captain knew the U-boat could be watching and waiting for a ship to stop and pick up the survivors.

Just as *The Usworth* slowed down, the Polish escort destroyer arrived and signalled she would circle around while *Usworth* picked up the survivors. *The Usworth* slowly got alongside the lifeboat.

Some of the crew scrambled down the nets to help the burnt and injured up to the safety of *The Usworth's* deck. Some were very badly burned, some just shocked and frightened.

As the last seaman was pulled from the lifeboat, *The Usworth* signalled the Polish escort, 'Thanks for being my shepherd,' and proceeded to rejoin the convoy.

Just as *The Usworth* regained her allotted position *The Felling* blew up with a gigantic roar; the sea around her heaved *The Usworth* into the air, causing huge waves which made the ships near her roll violently, and the hot air blast covered *The Usworth*.

Next morning O'Dell was sent down to the hospital to get the log of the hospital's casualties and the rest of the survivors. On the way down he passed one of the Signal Ratings talking to a Deck Rating. He heard him say, 'I'm telling you that ginger-headed bastard is one of them to blame.' As he was in a hurry, and also because in those days

Boy Seamen did not stop to listen to their seniors talking, he never heard the answer from the Deck Rating, but realised once again that the Signal Rating was talking about the ginger-headed Scot.

The log from the hospital made unhappy reading. Four of the survivors had died, seven more were suffering badly from severe steam and fire burns; nine others were suffering minor injuries and shock, but these would be fit to transfer to Number 3 hold in a couple of days.

No officers had been picked up from T*he Felling* and it had to be assumed that they'd all perished along with the second lifeboat.

No-one could survive in that temperature longer than twenty four hours. It was now twenty degrees below freezing.

Next morning everyone on the bridge was feeling subdued and tired, and never dreamed that this was just a minor prelude of the sheer hell that was to come.

The rest of the morning passed uneventfully, but in the afternoon, as darkness was closing in, a German Condor airplane was spotted astern of the convoy. They had all heard of the German Condor that was sent off from Norway to search out for a convoy trying to reach Russia.

Now everyone, from the Commodore to the youngest Boy Seaman, knew that this was it, that the Condor would radio their position to its base and to all U-boats in the area. All they could hope and pray for was fog, or extremely bad weather.

The temperature dropped to seventeen degrees, and for all their Arctic clothing they started to really feel the cold.

It soon became obvious that the Condor had fulfilled its role when, as night fell, the first torpedo struck. It was the American *S.S. Dallas* that had been so kind to us in Iceland that was hit.

In one mighty roar she blew. The whole night seemed to come alight. The sea heaved and the waves flung themselves into the air. Then there was complete darkness, as a searing hot wave of air rushed over *The Usworth*.

The *S.S. Dallas* had vanished.

The escort destroyers raced around, laying patterns of depth charges; but it soon became obvious there was more than one U-boat in this attack.

Two ships on the port side of the convoy were hit, *M.V. Bladon* and *S.S. Seaton. The Usworth* was again ordered to try to find the survivors.

As the two ships fell away, *The Usworth* slowly circled around them, at the same time giving them a wide berth as it became obvious that neither ship had any steering power.

Eventually a lamp blinking from the *M.V. Bladon* informed *Usworth* she had launched the lifeboats she had left, requesting *Usworth* to pick them up, and thanking *Usworth* for help.

Once again the wonderful seamanship of the Captain, M. Robertson R.N.R., proved itself. Dropping astern about half a mile, he brought the ship slowly up, and there on the starboard bow it was just possible to see the flicking of the little red light on the lifejackets as the waves lifted the lifeboats.

The Usworth slowly approached the boats. There were three of them: one motorboat, which was towing the other two.

Whoever was in charge on the motorboat had the sense to realise what *The Usworth* intended to do, so he turned his boat until he was moving parallel with her, and soon all three lifeboats were alongside.

The state of the *M.V. Bladon* crew was appalling.

The tannoy opened up, with the Jimmy telling all hands not on watch to move fast, for there were still U-Boats around.

The wounded were brought up first, *The Usworth* crew climbing down the netting to help. Most of them were on board when tannoy orders were, 'All hands back on board and cast off the three boats.' In a frantic struggle they emptied the boats and cast them off, but even so, as *The Usworth* swung violently to Port there were still some of the crew clinging to the recovery nets. But all managed to scramble on board.

Three more ships were lost before the night was out, and one U-boat was sunk. The night was bitter cold, penetrating through the Arctic clothing as they stood watch on the outer wings of the bridge.

The morning brought twilight glow, and *The Usworth* was ordered to fall away from the convoy to search for survivors. This was their job, and as the convoy steamed ahead the Captain spoke on the tanhoy, reminding all hands to keep a sharp look-out.

'We are going to find those survivors,' he said.

26

Tired and cold as they were, there was going to be no respite.

It was bitterly cold. Another theory taught at school turned out to be a myth. Salt water did freeze, as every little wave splashed on board proved. As soon as it hit the deck, it froze.

Deck Ratings not on look-out had the steam hoses going full blast, and the engineers, blacksmiths and electricians moved around the deck doing repairs. At last everyone appreciated the work that had been done in Cardiff dry dock, especially in accommodation, where the plywood and sawdust were proving such a blessing as insulation against the cold.

In the Port wing of the bridge O'Dell kept watch with Miles Kemp. Leading Seaman Brown and Boy Seaman Placid Gomes kept watch on the Starboard wing of the bridge. Bunts had put them on look-out while he, with another Signal Rating, kept signal watch.

It was now nearly twenty degrees below, the wind so bitter that even their breath was freezing into their balaclavas, and they had to keep the wool from sticking to their lips and the skin around their mouths. Everyone tried breathing through their nose and all usual chit chat was kept to a minimum, frozen wool stuck to one's flesh not being appreciated.

Suddenly some lifeboats were spotted, and the ship heeled over as she changed course towards them. O'Dell and Brown were ordered to leave their positions and assist at the nets.

Slowly they approached the lifeboats. It seemed everyone in the boats was asleep, or dead. There was not a movement as they edged closer.

O'Dell felt that everyone manning the nets was experiencing, as he was, a deep apprehension of what they were going to find.

Then C.P.O. Lack spoke, his voice firm but full of compassion.

'Now lads, let's get these poor bastards on board. Chop chop. And no tears. Remember your tears will freeze damn fast, and a blind seaman is no good to those poor devils in the boats.'

Then they were alongside, the crew scrambled down the nets.

It seemed at first that everyone in the lifeboats was indeed dead. All their clothing and boots were covered in ice: the water in the bottom of the boats was frozen, and some of the survivors had their feet trapped hard in the ice.

Hammers and iron bars were lowered down to break the ice and release the poor seamen.

Once they started to transfer the bodies to *The Usworth* there was movement in the boats; not much—an arm here, a leg there, some heads raised their faces encrusted in a thin film of ice. As gently, but as fast as possible they were transferred out of the boats. Those dead were laid out on deck, the others rushed below to the hospital, and once the transfer was complete the boats were released.

For the next two hours they searched for more survivors, at the same time keeping a sharp look out because the German plane had returned to keep them company.

Just as their Captain was thinking of rejoining the convoy, two more boats were spotted. They were lying about six hundred yards apart from each other. *The Usworth* closed in on the nearest one, and it soon became obvious that they were in a similar state to the other boats. Just as the survivors were about to be transferred, an urgent message came through from the Commodore: the convoy was under air attack and *The Usworth's* anti-aircraft guns were needed at once. She was to break off the search and rejoin the convoy, 'at once, repeat at once.'

The O.O.D.'s voice came over the tannoy to release the lifeboat and pull the nets up. The convoy was under attack and *The Usworth* was urgently needed. Even as he spoke the ship started to surge forward. The boat had only been half emptied when they released it, and the other boats were not even approached.

The Captain knew that for the Commodore to break radio silence the convoy must be in serious trouble, and although some of the crew did not appreciate what was happening and felt the Captain should have stopped at least a little longer to pick up everyone, those who were navy trained and not H.O.'s realised that there had been no choice.

This did not prevent some of the H.O.'s muttering among themselves that they would report the Captain when the ship reached the U.K.

In the meantime *H.M.S. Usworth* raced to help the convoy, but half a mile from it she came under her first air attack. From the starboard side three German Junker Torpedo planes attacked, releasing their torpedoes then racking the ship with their armour piercing shells. Every gun on *The Usworth* opened up with such a barrage that the enemy planes could not get close enough to be effective with the torpedoes. The ship swerved and swayed and zigzagged desperately. The noise was terrific, but the ship beat off the attack and rejoined the convoy.

Even in the midst of this horror the Commodore signalled, 'Thanks for coming. Have a good innings.' Frightened as he was at the time O'Dell remembered how proud he had felt when ordered to signal the reply, 'Hope to knock up a six Sir.'

The convoy was in a really bad way; at least four more merchant ships had been sunk, two of them tankers with their cargo of high octane so urgently needed by hard pressed Russians.

From the Commodore's point of view, he guessed the loss of one destroyer and one Cam Aircraft Carrier, which was slowly sinking, was a near disaster.

Since there were only about four hours of daylight in these latitudes at this time of the year, with the last wave of German planes beaten off and the darkness closing in the Commodore felt confident that the air attacks from the Norway bases would cease for the day and not resume until daylight the next day.

The signal went out for all ships to stand down from full alert to alert, but reminding all ships that there were still U-boats around.

The Usworth was ordered to go to the assistance of the Cam Carrier (known in the fleet as Woolworth Carriers as they were usually ex-merchant ships, converted to hold a small flight deck). This one, *H.M.S. Royal Arch*, was an ex-Shell tanker, and manned by an assortment of Royal Navy Reserve, Merchant Navy and T124X.

It was soon obvious that the *Royal Arch* was in a bad way, sinking slowly by the head and listing to port.

It was quickly established between the ships' Captains that the *Royal Arch* should lower all the boats and rafts she could, and *The Usworth* would also throw into the sea some of her rafts, although one could not hold out much hope for anyone in those freezing seas for more than a few minutes.

Darkness was closing in fast as *The Usworth* moved astern to receive the *Royal Arch* lifeboats. The first of these let down in fairly calm, though bitterly freezing, sea and it was full of those badly injured. As they came alongside the net men once again scrambled down to help the wounded up. They were in a pitiful state: some badly burned, others wounded in the air attacks; some were blind, some had a leg or arm off. But O'Dell noticed in horror that there was no blood. Because it was so cold, blood just froze into a black clot. It looked to him like pictures he had seen in books of black pitch put on open wounds in Nelson's days, on the old wooden man-of-wars. He had wondered fleetingly what the old salts of Nelson's *Victory* would have made of the modern weapons.

C.P.O. Lack's voice called, 'Get a move on O'Dell,' and he came back to the present fast. He was at the top of the nets on deck, so that he and the others were heaving the wounded up the last part to the deck. After a while he realised the men coming up now were the last, and not in too bad a state.

A flurry of activity around him made him look down on the last boat. It held the only three officers to survive from the *Royal Arch*, plus their Captain. It was obvious that the Captain was in a bad way, seriously hurt, and the two Ratings scrambled down the nets to assist. The Jimmy No. 1 appeared to welcome the Captain aboard, and to convey *The Usworth's* Captain's respects.

When the wounded Captain, although badly hurt, held up tradition by being the last to leave his ship and gained the deck it was clear to all he was truly suffering. After trying to stand and return the Jimmy's salute, he wavered side to side, then keeled over. They rushed him to the hospital, but he was dead in an hour.

O'Dell was to remember that Captain's face for a long time to come in his dreams; remember the sheer horror of it. The left eye, part of the forehead and cheek had been torn away. That part of his head and mouth was just like black pitch. It was sheer guts that had kept him alive and, as the Captain of *The Usworth* was to say later, he had done his duty and got all those still alive off his ship before it had taken its last plunge.

It turned out later that the Captain, with two of the *Royal Arch* officers that were fit enough to attend with some of their crew, had buried the Captain of the *Royal Arch* in the graveyard watch, with full battle ensign and salute, over the stem, without even slowing down.

In the meantime the destroyer *Primulas* came alongside to transfer some more survivors she had picked up. Once again

Usworth's Captain had proved his first class seamanship, despite the pitch dark and freezing cold night.

Just as the transfer was complete, and everyone off watch thought they could now get their heads down for a well-earned kip, the alarm bells rang, and the convoy was under another U-boat attack.

O'Dell remembered how tired he felt, but fear soon woke him as a merchant ship in front of them was hit, blowing up with a great roar. A ball of fire lit up the whole convoy, then, as the heat washed over the bridge, she was gone. It took a moment to realise she had completely disappeared, leaving everyone on the bridge gaping in awe, and fear: the fear and feeling of being trapped in hell, insidiously and slowly percolated the entire bridge.

Bunts, with the Navigating Officer's permission, stood all the signal section down, with the exception of himself and two ratings, ordering them to wash, then get their heads down.

In the talk while they were washing it transpired that Miles and Placid had felt ill and vomited while helping the survivors down to the hospital.

'How about you O'Dell?' asked Brown. 'How did you feel?'

He replied, 'Oh I felt funny all right, but you must remember I was at Tobruk, and there was no weather to freeze the blood. It just poured out, and I can assure you that I fainted and was sick then.'

In what seemed no time at all they were awakened by one of the Ratings. After a cup of hot cocoa and a bowl of burrgo they wrapped themselves up and reported to Bunts on the bridge.

O'Dell was shocked at Bunts' face. He had aged suddenly, and now really did look old.

Bunts gave Brown his orders, and allocated who should be on look out, and at signals on port and starboard wings, then put him and Kemp on messenger and running duties.

The sea had become more calm, although the temperature was still twenty degrees below.

It was a while before everyone realised that a fog was gently falling over the convoy, and then came the joy of realising it meant no air attacks. But there was recognition of the danger from ships that did not keep in their position.

They had of course covered such an eventuality in their final meeting at Iceland, but the Commodore signalled by lamp for all ships to remain vigilant, and to stay On Station. Any ship that could not, for any reason, was, as agreed, to flash all her lights for twenty seconds every five minutes to warn ships in close proximity. If however all power was lost they were to use fog flares and horn.

The fog soon became very thick, and brought with it another danger. The misty fog froze to ice as soon as it landed on the ship and the crew's heavy weather gear. Those still out on deck with steam hoses soon found their headgear frozen solid. Orders were given for all hands to remain inside unless it was urgent. All gunners and look outs were recalled into the accommodation or, in the case of the wing men, to inside the bridge.

Two hours later the Commodore's worst fears were realised as the Merchant Ship *S.S. Ankerat* of the Celtic Steamship Company broke down, and with her loss of power, being unable even to steer, she became like a rogue elephant, all eight thousand ton of her. She lumbered all over the place. The ships around her moved this way and that, at the same time being restricted from too much movement, to avoid other ships at their stations. Unable to break radio silence called for calm nerves and first class seamanship from all merchant ships, and they were not found wanting. The *S.S. Ankerat* fell away, but in the fog could not be seen clearly and everyone on *Usworth's* bridge strained their eyeballs at look out posts.

Then the lights of flares from *S.S. Ankerat* were seen from astern. Although it only looked like a candle flicker, everyone heaved a sigh of relief, at least the ship was clear of the convoy.

O'Dell had been ordered to the hospital to collect the log. It made unhappy reading: forty two men seriously hurt, fifteen slightly hurt, sixty four survivors in the Number 3 Hatch accommodation; but seventy dead, and laid out aft, awaiting burial.

The Captain ordered the bodies into the sea; a terrible, but necessary job, and although *The Usworth* never actually stopped, she slowed down as much as the Captain judged safe. The watch detail plus gunners who had been stood down and survivors helped lower the bodies over the stern. They received a double tot, and everyone felt they had earned it. It left an awful feeling through the ship's very subdued crew.

Once again it took Bunts to put it into perspective.

'Well,' he said that evening in the Mess, 'we at least had the fog for cover. We would never have had a chance in daylight, the air attacks would have seen to that. At least we managed to bury the dead in peace.'

One of the gunners O'Dell had become friendly with, a young eighteen year old from Sunderland, told him later that it had been awful. Some of the dead had been lying there so long that they had frozen to the deck. Other bodies had all become frozen together, and they had an awful time separating them. In the end they had used the steam hose to scrape the frozen bodies off the deck.

'Not a pretty sight,' he said. 'One I shall never forget.'

After a peaceful night without U-boats around, everyone felt at least a little rested. The freezing fog was still with them although not so thick as it had been. O'Dell just hoped it would stay a couple more days; it was better to risk a ship breaking down than air attacks.

He had just gone on watch when a most terrifying noise, like a London Underground train, went right over the ship. It was frightening: a cushion of air seemed to suck them upwards. He could have sworn afterwards that his feet had left the deck.

'What the hell was that?' he said.

Brown shouted. 'They are heavy shells. Must be a big ship around.'

The alarm went off, everyone closed up for action stations, but after five more heavy shells they heard no more, and although the heavy ships, protecting the convoy, had moved out to intercept, they saw and found nothing.

Bunts later told them in the Mess that the Captain and officers were of the opinion that a German heavy battle wagon had been sent out from Norway to try and frighten the convoy into dispersing, so leaving the ships more vulnerable to the enemy U-boats and aircraft, once the fog had lifted.

By mid-morning the fog started to lift, and he witnessed one of the awful aspects of war. Two of the crew were up near the bows, frozen to death. It was a grotesque tableau. From what the seamen could see it would appear the first man must have slipped and fallen on the frozen deck, his mate had stopped to bend over to give him a hand up,

33

when a small wave must have broken over the bows, turned to ice and imprisoned both seamen. Trapped as they were, in the thick fog with no-one aware of the situation, they had died frozen together. It gave one a funny feeling to behold them.

Once more the steam hose was brought into use to free the two men, and they were put over the side straight away. It was, as the gunner had said, not a pretty sight.

Although the fog had lifted slightly, and it was possible to make out the shapes of the ships ahead, there were no more air attacks, but the German Condor, ever watchful, had returned to haunt them.

As night fell the *S.S. Ankerat* broke radio silence. She had been torpedoed on her way to rejoin the convoy. She reported that she had launched two lifeboats.

There was no attack that night, but the weather worsened, and *The Usworth* started to roll badly, and pitch. Then it started to snow. The temperature went up to only fifteen degrees below.

Going on watch at 0400 hours, O'Dell felt more rested, but the snowing had stopped, and by 0800 hours it started to turn to a faint dusky dawn. Somehow he knew it was going to be a hard day.

They had just finished breakfast and were having a chat before turning in, when the alarm went off. Putting on their heavy weather gear and helmets, they rushed to the bridge, just as the first wave of enemy aircraft struck.

This time they were ready, and every gun on every ship in the convoy, both Navy and Merchant Navy, put up such a barrage of fire power that the Germans had to release their torpedoes and bombs a lot higher and further away than they had hoped to do. But they still persevered: wave after wave flew out at the convoy from their base in Norway.

The Usworth's intense fire power left the decks covered with empty shell cases, and those survivors not already engaged in supplying ammunition, or keeping watch with the fire crew, turned to put the empty cases over the side.

At last the short span of daylight drew to a close, and the air attacks slowly petered out, with only two ships lost.

Such was the feeling of relief that, two weeks before, the loss of two ships would have been a disaster, it now seemed an acceptable loss. Everyone felt so utterly drained and fatigued, and frightened.

The Usworth was ordered to drop astern to search for survivors, but found none.

When O'Dell and Kemp and the others got to their Mess, they found some of the aircraft strafing had unfortunately cut through the steam pipes, and no heat or water was available.

Everyone was so tired and worn out. He felt drained of any strength; even enough to join in the grouses and moans.

Chapter Three

After a cup of stewed tea from the doggy and a corned beef sandwich they all fell into their bunks. As sleep claimed him, O'Dell's last thoughts were of his old ship, which had no steam or water in any accommodation and he wondered what these lads would have made of that.

It seemed but a few moments before the alarm went: 'Action Stations.' As they all stumbled around for the heavy weather gear the first real sign of the strain and stress emerged. Two of the Boy Seamen were trying to stop themselves from crying, while one of the Ratings broke down altogether. Leading Hand Brown took charge of him, and O'Dell heard Brown saying, 'Come on, buck up! Don't let the German bastards get you down!' He heard no more as he rushed to the bridge and got there just as a tanker blew up. It was the *M.V. Briny Bal*. The ball of fire was appalling! Fear gripped him; he felt too frightened to move and had no control over his body functions. He knew he had messed his clothes.

He heard the Captain saying to the O.O.W., 'Poor bastards, they never stood a chance. I knew the Master of the tanker well.'

Most of the Officers were by this time on the bridge, and even in the middle of the U-boat's attack the thought crossed his mind that they all looked so immaculate; all were washed and shaved, yet they must be feeling as fatigued as the rest of the ship's personnel, if not more, for they had the added strain of responsibility.

Two more explosions brought his thoughts back to the present. It became clear it was a concerted U-boat attack. Well organised attacks came from all around the convoy. The escort destroyers laid down pattern after pattern of depth charges, which helped keep the U-boats down, but some managed to get their torpedoes off just the same.

H.M.S. Primulas and *H.M.S. Offa* got a U-boat, bringing it to the surface, where *The Offa* finished her off.

After two more hours 'Stand Down' was given, and when O'Dell went straight to the wash-house he found he was not the only one with dirty clothes.

In fatigue, fear and frustration they collapsed into their bunks, hammocks and locker tops to fall into a shallow sleep, their nerves screaming out for release from tension and thoughts of death.

In the dawn break *The Usworth* was ordered to search for survivors, and as it got lighter they spotted a lifeboat; but they found the four seamen in her frozen to death, and let the boat drift away.

When *The Usworth* rejoined the convoy the Commodore ordered her to resume her station, after thanking the Captain for his efforts in the search for survivors.

The temperature dropped to twenty four below. The ship was still on double watch and look-out. It was now so cold their breath just froze around the mouth of their balaclavas, so talking was kept to a minimum, and at last the Captain ordered extra watch keepers and look-outs to stand down; a sigh of relief could be heard through the whole ship.

That night the U-boats returned, but thanks to the wonderful defensive style of the escorts not one U-boat got near enough to fire its weapon of death.

The German Air Force struck again the next day. Wave after wave of planes flew at the convoy, and once more every gun on every ship opened up. But the Germans pressed home their attack, even more strongly than before, and after each run to release torpedo or bomb they returned to rake the convoy with armour-piercing shells and machine guns.

This created havoc on the ships, not only destroying lifeboats and rafts and killing a lot of Gunners, but also killing those on the ships' bridges, causing these ships to fall away from their station; this in turn caused other ships to move out of their stations. It was in fact a domino effect, causing havoc and destruction, to the delight of the enemy, until the ships got new Officers on their bridges and were able to resume their allotted positions.

At last darkness moved in and the air attacks ceased.

Each ship licked its wounds: *The Usworth's* deck was littered with the dead, some just arms and legs. Receiving the Captain's permission, the Jimmy No.1 collected C.P.O. Lack and other P.O. deck and engine room hands, and made a clean sweep from bows to stern, putting all bodies and part bodies over the side, using steam hoses where necessary to scrape away those frozen to gun emplacements and free the deck. Everyone by this time was too far gone from sheer fatigue and stress to worry about proper burials. As the Captain rightly surmised: out of sight, out of mind.

No-one could have dreamt at that period the anguish the Captain was to suffer over his decision, as he was a strong, dedicated and committed Christian.

Gradually the convoy got back into a resemblance of order and positions, chivvied on by the escorts, who must have had their own sick and dead to worry about.

As the Canadian destroyer went past *The Usworth* she lamped, 'Bad business.'

The Captain snapped back. 'Not too bad, thanks to you and other escorts.'

Darkness had fallen when the Captain spoke on the tannoy. He thanked everyone for their hard work and efforts, especially the Gunners, who had three enemy planes confirmed as being shot down, and he continued, 'Now the good news. We are now out of range of any land-based aircraft, so from now on we only have the U-boats to worry about. Also if the weather holds we should be in Russian waters in the next three to four days.' He finished with, 'Good night, and keep your faith in God.'

In the signal quarters it was confirmed that two Boy Seamen had been killed, also one Rating. Another Rating had gone off his head and had to be locked away. Miles Kemp had been injured and was in hospital.

Everyone was sick, miserable and utterly exhausted. Fear, really deep fear, was everyone's companion. Only Bunts carried on as usual, but even he looked at least twenty years older; somehow he helped to keep them all sane, and to allay their fears by acting so normally.

O'Dell asked for, and got permission to go to the hospital to inquire about Kemp, but on reaching the outer sickbay he ran straight into Kemp, who was on his way back to the section. It turned out that he had not been injured in action but had slipped on deck, lost his glove and grabbed the rail, which was so cold he could not let go. They had poured water on the rail and his hand to effect his release. His hand was bad, very bad: the inside palm and fingers had all skin and flesh torn off, while the back of his hand was badly scalded and blistered.

Although doped with morphine, Kemp gave a smile. 'Well, that's me out of action!' he said.

O'Dell remembered grinning back and saying, 'I doubt Bunts will let you off that easily and lightly.'

On their way back to quarters Kemp said, 'O'Dell, can I ask you something personal?'

He replied, 'Sure. But don't expect an answer if it's too personal!'

'Are you frightened? Are you afraid to die?'

'Of course I am,' he replied. 'Why do you ask?'

'It's just that you and Leading Hand Brown don't seem to worry like the rest of the mess, and one of the Ratings said it's because you and Brown have no family or home so you don't care.'

'What a stupid thing to say,' he replied. 'Of course I'm frightened, and fear is eating away at me just the same as at everyone else. Believe me, I have very strong reasons to live. You must understand Brown and I have been brought up in a very hard school where we learnt to control our facial expressions more than the average person.'

'Was your life really as hard as Brown alleges?' asked Kemp.

They had reached the door of their quarters and, and O'Dell hesitated. Then he said, 'Miles, you can have no conception unless you were there. If we survive this voyage, and you are still interested, I promise to tell you about it.'

'You promise?' said Kemp.

'I promise,' he replied.

He had guessed right about Kemp getting back to work. Bunts soon told Kemp that he only had the night off, and the next day he was to assist the look-outs. However, it was not to be, for next morning Kemp had a raging fever and kept calling for his mother. Bunts detailed two Ratings to take him to the hospital.

O'Dell remembered afterwards he was just reaching the bridge and thinking of poor Kemp when the first torpedo hit them.

The Usworth heaved and gave a great shudder. Just as the Captain started to give orders another torpedo struck right under the bridge, port side on.

O'Dell heard a great roar, and felt himself floating in the air. The noise around him was sheer bedlam, and the heat so intense that each breath was like sucking a flame into his mouth.

Chapter Four

It seemed hours, but in reality was only a few moments, before he managed to open his eyes. He felt someone pull his left arm and looked up. Brown was mouthing something, but the blast had deafened him. With Brown's help he got to his feet; some of his heavy weather gear was on fire and smouldering, so he banged and slapped his hands all over himself. Brown slapped his back and together they put out the fire.

Looking around the bridge all they could see was a shambles. The Quartermaster, Signal Rating and both Officers were dead, or at least appeared dead. He saw that the Captain had somehow got to his feet, swaying, and he heard the Captain's Tiger assuring him he would find his hat for him. The Tiger kept repeating, 'You must not be on the bridge without your hat Sir.'

Looking for a hat? O'Dell heard some hysterical laughter, then Brown slapped his face.

'Snap out of it O'Dell.'

Another slap and he realised it was he that was laughing. He heard Brown repeat, 'Snap out of it O'Dell. Remember the Naval School and don't let us down.' By this time the Jimmy Number One and Bunts had reached what was left of the bridge.

Once it was established that all communication to and from the bridge had been destroyed, the Captain ordered Jimmy Number One to inform the engine room and then to organise every available hand to transfer the sick and the injured to the boats.

Then O'Dell heard the order that he had dreaded all trip.

'ABANDON SHIP.'

The Captain then gave Brown the order to take all Boy Seamen from every section and see them on a lifeboat. Bunts was to stay with the Captain on the bridge.

As they struggled to reach the boats through the twisted and hot metal he'd volunteered to go and collect Miles Kemp from the hospital while Brown got the other boys together.

'Right,' said Brown, 'but make it snappy O'Dell.'

40

As he was rushing towards the hospital, *The Usworth* was hit for the third time. The ship jumped and lurched: the noise was horrific as the twisted steel plates screamed and burst apart with rivet heads flying every way, cutting through everything and everyone, including the crew.

Before his eyes he witnessed the horror of rivet heads slicing men's bodies, legs and heads as sure and as efficient as any machine gun bullet. But there was no blood-just black pitch.

Then he felt a great bang in his back and legs. The pain was terrific and he knew he was falling. He could hear someone screaming in pain and agony, sheer agony, and just as he passed into merciful oblivion he realised the screamer was himself.

He woke to the sound of strange voices, yelling and screaming, then the pain seemed to wash over him and he drifted into a dark void. He vaguely remembered coming to now and then, swimming to the surface till the pain took over, then merciful release came as the darkness carried him away.

A voice was calling his name: 'O'Dell! O'Dell!' over and over again. Where was he who kept calling? Was it a Master? Or was it an Officer?

Then he felt a vicious pain across his forehead and tried to open his eyes, but could not see. Fear took hold and temporarily banished the pain. He was blind! He could not see!

Self pity took over. Oh no! Not blind! Not after all he had been through!

He heard a voice saying, 'No O'Dell, you're not blind. There are bandages over your eyes and face. You are strapped to your bunk to prevent any movement on your part. Can you hear me O'Dell?' Relief washed over him: he was not blind. He heard someone assuring him he was going to be alright, that the worst was over.

Pain claimed him again; once more he fainted away. It was a merciful respite.

Later he woke and tried to move, then remembered someone telling him he was lashed to his bunk. He licked his lips and tried to speak, but only managed a croak.

It was marvellous to hear the welcome voice of Bunts.

'Oh, so you're awake at last O'Dell.'

He tried again to speak but his mouth was too dry.

'Don't try to talk. Just suck this,' said Bunts, putting a tube into his mouth. He gratefully sucked up the water. What a glorious drink!

'Not too much at a time, it will only run straight out of you into your tin and we will have to empty it,' said Bunts. 'If you can hear me just nod, O'Dell, and I will tell you the situation.'

He gave a nod, and received a sharp stab of pain in return.

'You are in a hospital, at a place called Ekonomaya. You have been here for two weeks and you have been knocked around a bit, but they have operated on you twice and removed all the shrapnel and parts of rivet heads. However as most of the damage is around your private parts, back and front, also your upper thighs, you will have to pass water through a tube in your right side down to a tin; a large tin.

You are lashed to your bunk to stop you throwing yourself around, and re-opening your wounds. We had to take you back once, and the Russian doctor was not very happy because they are very short of medical supplies here. To avoid a repeat the Captain's orders were to lash you down.

You are bandaged up because of the blast on the bridge. Your eyebrows are burnt or singed and you will find it difficult to talk for a while as your mouth is burnt inside. But the Russian doctor has assured the Captain that all the burns will heal and he doesn't think there will be any permanent scars.'

Next time he came to he heard a lot of talking around his bunk, but not in a language he understood. A lady spoke.

'Please nod if you are awake.'

He gave a nod.

'I am the interpreter,' she continued. 'The doctor says good morning, and for you not to worry. He feels you are over the worst, as long as you rest and do not move. Movement is very bad for you. The doctor also says he hopes to take off the bandages in a few days. In the meantime orderlies will take care of you and see to your wants.'

He heard them move away, then one returned: it was the interpreter. She said, 'The doctor asked me return to inquire your age please?' He managed to croak, 'Sixteen years.'

'Thank you! The doctor is most interested.'

A few days later the doctor returned with a nurse and the

interpreter, and took off the bandages around his head and eyes. He could see them now. This was his first view of the Russian Allies, but he still couldn't see clearly. There seemed to be a thin brown film over his eyes that made everything and everyone look slightly brown.

The interpreter said, 'The doctor asks how you are feeling and how well can you see?'

He explained that everything looked light brown.

After a few words with the doctor the interpreter said. 'The doctor says that is caused by the blast and the sheets of flame you went through, but it will fade slowly over maybe two or three years.'

The doctor then examined the rest of his body, and through the interpreter explained all they had done to him, adding again they had every hope of him having a full recovery as long as he didn't move.

The interpreter went on to explain they had no more morphine nor any chloroform and that any more operations would have to be done without any pain killers, which would be a very painful process, 'So no movements please.'

He asked the interpreter to thank the doctor for all he had done on his behalf, and assured him there would be no repeats of throwing himself around. He added he would like to tell the doctor that he was deeply sorry for causing any extra work. This she did. The doctor smiled and leaned over and patted his shoulder, saying something at the same time.

The interpreter smiled. 'The doctor says it's alright. You are very brave in fact. Nearly as brave as a Russian!'

Then they all smiled and moved off.

He smiled with them, as he drifted off to sleep. Later he woke to find Bunts sitting beside his bunk, who said that he was glad to see the bandages off, although the yellow stuff the Russkies had smothered him with was not nice to look at. Still, as long as it did the trick, that's all that mattered.

He explained to Bunts about everything looking brown.

Chapter Five

'Oh great!' said Bunts. 'We will all have a sun tan, which we could do with in this cold hole. Seriously, O'Dell, if the doctor says it will fade gradually, then it will. He is a world famous doctor. It appears he upset Stalin, who banished him out here in the deep freezing north barren land. Moscow's loss is our gain.'

Bunts went on: 'Another thing, he can speak perfect English, but is not allowed to do so. He must use the Interpreter at all times or he will be sent to a detention camp.'

Bunts then told him that Miles Kemp had lost his hand; the doctor had to amputate it to save the arm. Brown had survived and was in a naval camp outside Murmansk.

Most of the officers and crew of *The Usworth* and the survivors they had picked up had perished.

'In fact O'Dell,' Bunts said, 'as far as we can ascertain, only twenty one survived: three officers, seventeen crew and, of course, the Captain. So you can count yourself lucky. At least you're alive.'

Bunts left and he drifted off to sleep, but deep sleep was not to be had. The pain came back wave after wave. He gritted his teeth in a determined effort not to yell, and just as the pain eased off the Captain arrived and sat down beside his bunk.

'Well young man,' he said, 'Glad to see you're awake. Bunts tells me you're feeling better, which is good news. You certainly had us worried for a while.'

O'Dell felt embarrassed with the Captain sitting so near and talking to him. He was tongue-tied and very gauche, but the Captain appeared not to notice, and he went on to explain that all the ship's papers had gone down with the ship, as had all the paymaster's section, so no records of individuals' home addresses, next of kin, or wages were available regarding the survivors of *Usworth*. 'When you feel stronger, O'Dell,' he said, 'perhaps you would be kind enough to let me or Bunts have your details, although I can't promise anything. The Russkies are not being very helpful.'

The Captain went on to say that there was a Royal Navy doctor on his way from Archangel. Although he was officially coming to inspect the hospital and medical facilities, the Captain had hopes of using the doctor's good offices to get news to the survivors' next of kin.

After the Captain left, O'Dell tried to take stock of the ward, but as he could not raise himself, he soon gave up the idea and started to think about what the Old Man had said. Particulars of next of kin? There was only his sister: she was still in North Africa, serving in the A.T.S., as far as he was aware.

He wondered what his sister was doing. What would she have made of this terrible Arctic weather, so bitterly cold and hostile?

Who would have thought, when he had met up with his sister in Alexandria just a few months ago in that stinking heat and smell, that he would be lying here, so badly hurt, in this cold, cruel, harsh country?

Two days later the Royal Navy doctor arrived. He appeared to be about thirty years old, and after going around the ward, speaking to everyone and examining one or two of the more serious cases, he arrived a the foot of O'Dell's bunk.

The Captain, who was escorting the doctor, said, 'This is our Boy Seaman S. T. O'Dell R268793. O'Dell, this is Doctor Lieutenant Commander Fisher.'

The doctor smiled, and moving alongside the bunk he said, 'So this is the young man everyone is talking about? What's this I hear? You keep throwing yourself about and they have to keep you strapped in?'

'I do it in my sleep Sir,' O'Dell replied. 'I certainly don't know I'm doing it!'

The doctor bent towards his face, took a hard long look and said, 'I don't think you'll have any marks when you heal. Now tell me do you still have a brown film over your eyes?'

'Yes, Sir.'

'Well, there's not much we can do about that here. The medical facilities are very primitive, to say the least, but once we get you home, we will soon sort you out. But it must be said that it's doubtful if you can stay in the Signal section, if you can stay in the Service at all. I understand you're T124X. Maybe you would be better back in the Merchant Navy.'

45

After arranging that he would be helped to sit up, and told the doctor would be seeing him at 0900 hours next day for a full examination, the doctor left.

Once the hospital orderlies, under the nurse's supervision, had sat him up with extra padded wood for a back rest and more pillows, he was at last able to survey the ward.

It was a stark and crudely built ward, made of rough-hewed half logs of newly cut down trees, and put together so primitively and crudely that in some places there were gaps nearly half an inch wide, where the wind constantly blew in. When it snowed, the snow came in, making life very uncomfortable for all.

The ward housed ten injured seamen, plus Bunts, who helped the interpreter and liaised between the wards and the Russians. It would seem that Bunts could still remember some Russian he had learnt in his 1920 stint, and that, with the lessons given to him by the interpreter every day, made Bunts, according to the Captain, worth his weight in gold.

Two large pot-bellied stoves were kept going day and night, but even so there was often ice to be found on the stark rough wood walls in the mornings.

It was a while before O'Dell found out that the poor orderlies were Finnish prisoners of war, who had to go out cutting down trees after working all night so that there was always wood on hand. Every evening these orderlies unrolled two large rolls of tarpaulin and covered the bunks, then took them off in the mornings and shook the snow off outside. How he blessed those tarpaulin covers! They not only helped to keep him dry, but warm as well.

He discovered that the hospital orderlies were not allowed to speak to anyone except the Russians and Bunts. Any deviation from this order could mean death, or being sent back to the harsher camps where they were set to work, either on the docks or building harbour defences in the bitter viscous cold of under twenty degrees.

Bunts impressed on the patients that talking to the orderlies was doing no-one a favour, least of all the Finnish prisoners.

Next morning the two orderlies carried O'Dell to a large room, where they carefully laid him on a rough-hewn board.

The Royal Navy and Russian doctors, accompanied by the nurse, the interpreter and the Captain, proceeded to carry out a slow and thorough examination of his body. It was painful, but above all it was cold!

They moved away to hold a long discussion, then returned.

The Royal Navy doctor did the talking. He said that after two operations, and wonderful achievements by the Russian doctor and his staff, which he, as a doctor, could not fault, they had decided, taking everything into consideration, that they felt it only right to let him know the truth. 'We feel, O'Dell, that you have proved you can take it. O'Dell, we are truly sorry, but it's our considered opinion that you have only a fifty-fifty chance of ever walking again.'

The Royal Navy doctor went on to explain that the shrapnel and rivet heads had cut through. his body, slicing different nerves, blood lines, sperm lines-but it all went over his head. All he could hear as the doctor droned on and on, was that he had only a fifty-fifty chance of ever walking again.

This phrase repeated itself over and over in his head. A wave of self-pity swept over him, then the black rage returned, the red screen came over his eyes, and he heard himself screaming.

'NO! NO!'

He tried to move, but they moved as one to hold him down, yelling for the orderlies to come to help.

Now he was coming out of the black tunnel, and he could see the light ahead. He heard Bunts saying, 'Are you awake O'Dell?' He gave a nod, then it all came back. Wave after wave of self-pity swept over him. He felt tears pouring down his face and felt Bunt's hand on his shoulder.

'Go on, son. Get it out and over.'

He felt his whole body racking and shaking, his mouth opening and shutting without uttering a sound as he tried to sob and to cry.

Then the words came.

'Why me? Haven't I suffered enough? Why me? I don't want to live if I can't walk.' The words came out in a scream.

Bunts just kept quietly saying, 'Let it go, son. Just let it go!' at the same time still gently patting his shoulder.

After a while he felt calmer. Bunts put a tube to his mouth, and he drank deeply. It was a drink he had never tasted before. It burnt his sore mouth, but at the same time knocked him out completely.

At sixteen years of age he'd had his first taste of vodka.

It came to give him peaceful release from his unhappiness.

His return to the land of the living came during the night. Although he was lashed down again, he found he could move his head slightly and he could see the top of one of the stoves glowing red and one of the oil lamps swinging in the wind that was howling through the cracks.

He'd just started to feel sorry for himself again and was asking himself, 'Why me?' when from across the ward in the bunk opposite he heard a terrible cry of pain and anguish. Between the screams he heard someone moaning in a Scottish accent, 'God forgive me. Oh what have I done?'

He could just make out Bunts' head as he appeared at the side of the shouting man's bunk, and he could hear Bunts saying softly, 'Now, now, Scotty. Take it easy. Sorry we have no morphine.'

Moving his head over slightly, O'Dell could just see Bunts wiping the man's forehead. He heard the Scot say, 'The pain's awful Bunts. I suppose it's my punishment.'

'Don't talk daft, man,' replied Bunts, his Geordie accent coming to the fore.

The Scot moaned, then screamed. O'Dell felt sick to hear another human in such pain. It reminded him of Tobruk.

By this time everyone in the ward was awake, and although the other eight men had lost either an arm or a leg, in one case both, and another was blind, he sensed a wave of sympathy for the Scot. Sinclair was, after all, the only one who was definitely going to die. No matter how crippled we are, he thought, at least we are alive.

The hospital orderlies appeared, and Bunts spoke to them. One of them went off and returned with the Captain. He and Bunts spoke briefly in low voices, then the Captain spoke aloud to all of them.

'I expect you are all awake. I am sorry to have to tell you that our shipmate A. B. Blair Sinclair is dying.' And as if to confirm that statement, the Russian doctor and interpreter arrived.

The Captain went on, 'I shall say a prayer and a few words I can remember from the Bible. Then C.P.O. Emberton and myself will sing 'Abide with me'. I hope those of you who can will join us.'

The Captain's voice carried across the ward:

'We cry to Thee, oh Lord,

O Lord hear our prayer,

Let our cry come to Thee.'

The Captain's voice droned on and on; something about 'I am the life.' Then they were singing, and some of the lads joined in.

O'Dell thought of his life: the orphanage, the good times, the harsh and cruel times, the Naval School, and in particular Lieutenant Commander Yearly. He remembered the terrible slaughter off Tobruk, and wondered how two grown men, two great and wonderful seamen, could still believe in God after all they had been through.

He himself knew there was no such being, but if people need that kind of belief to face the world, so be it. As long as they did not preach to him over and over again.

The poor Scot gave another terrible cry of pain and whimpered something. The Captain's voice was full of compassion.

'Don't torment yourself, lad. God forgives all.'

A short time later the Captain announced to the ward that A.B. Blair Sinclair had crossed the bar, and had departed to a better place.

O'Dell remembered thinking it could hardly be a worse place.

Somehow he knew that A.B. Blair Sinclair was the ginger-headed Scot from *The Usworth*. He decided he really must find out what the Scot had done, and why the Signal Rating had disliked him so much, and what the Scot had done to make him feel so guilty.

The next day Miles Kemp took over Sinclair's bunk. O'Dell was overjoyed to see Kemp again. It seemed that Bunts had thought he could do with someone of his own age group: hence Miles' arrival.

From Miles he learnt there were actually three wards and theirs was considered the seriously injured ward.

Telling Miles how sorry he was that he had lost his hand, he was surprised at Miles' answer.

'Well,' Miles said, 'it could have been worse. At least I'm not blind, and at least I can walk.' Then, realising what he had said, he stopped. 'Oh hell, O'Dell, I never meant it to come out like that. I am stupid.'

O'Dell gave a little laugh to cover Miles' embarrassment and to stop him from worrying.

But Miles had fled the ward, which settled down into a daily routine. The Finnish hospital orderlies kept the fires going and the ward clean.

Among their other duties they helped carry and move any patient, according to the wishes of the doctor. The food was cooked in a small kitchen in the apex of the three adjoining wards, and the orderlies really tried to serve it hot.

In O'Dell's case it didn't matter, as he still could not take solid food, and was living on beef tea, watery custards, and semolina pudding. Miles told him there were tins and tins of beef extract, which was like Oxo. It came in five-pound tins: battle axe tins. There were also tins of jam, marmalade and margarine.

Around this time Bunts explained to the ward that as the Russian Army had its hands full at the moment with the German Army around Murmansk, the Russians were happy to let the Captain run the hospital as long as everyone obeyed the rules, and with the clear understanding that the Russian interpreter was in over-all command. Any deviation from the rules would have serious repercussions, they warned.

Bunts ended by saying again, 'For goodness sake, don't break the rules!'

The hospital was supplied with food collected from any ship that managed to reach port.

The Russkies provided an old army truck and armed guards for this. The Captain and Bunts would visit each ship and ask for food. Some gave, some didn't. Those that gave received a government receipt, but some ships were very short on supplies themselves.

Unfortunately if the Russian guards saw the Captain and Bunts leaving a ship empty handed, they fixed their bayonets, and no matter what was said by anyone, they raided the ship's storeroom, often taking more than the other ships had given freely. It therefore became necessary to warn each ship that it was better to give a little than for the guards to take a lot.

The hospital storeroom was well stocked with tinned soups, corned beef, Spam, dried peas, rice, beans, yeast, flour and, of course, condensed milk, which the lads called Connie Onnie; plus the battle axe tins, which all weighed between five and ten pounds. If any ship spared any fish or meat, it was hung in the hospital passageway: it was so cold there that no fridge was necessary.

The Russkies did not, it seemed, want any of the food, but seemed to go on Cloud Nine for Welsh boiled sweets. As it was the opinion of most seafarers that these sweets were boiled from horses' hooves, the Russkies were welcome to them.

All this O'Dell learned from Bunts during his very welcome visits.

Now O'Dell was able to sit up, with the help of the lads and the padded wood, and could join in the daily brainwashing sessions given by the interpreter, as she extolled the great virtue of Communism as opposed to the Western denigrated democracy. He enjoyed them at first, having had no ideals of any political party at home.

He learned a lot about the Labour and Conservative parties, as well as how Russia was run. When the interpreter realised he was truly a virgin in politics, she really started to give him the full treatment, but every statement she made was seen as a challenge by someone in the ward.

One day she lost her temper, and shouted, 'Have any of you every visited the Gorbals in Glasgow?'

This caused a loud outcry of 'Unfair!' It was not a true representation of the average life-style in the United Kingdom, any more than the port of Ekomonaya represented the average life-style of Russia.

Someone pointed out that Stepney in London was the same as the Gorbals, and O'Dell was just going to say that he had lived in Stepney for a while, when a voice full of bitterness said, 'That's where that bastard Sinclair lived. In the bloody Gorbals.'

Bunts quickly jumped in.

'That's enough of that. The man is dead.' O'Dell couldn't help himself.

'What did he do wrong? he asked Bunts.

There was complete silence in the ward. Then Bunts said to O'Dell, 'When we have our talk tonight I will try and give a fair and impartial version. Until then I don't want to hear Sinclair mentioned.'

O'Dell sank back on to his padded board. He felt an excited tingle.

At last he was going to hear all about Sinclair. He could hardly contain himself. Roll on 1830 hours, he thought.

Bunts organised a kind of talking forum at night, to last from 1830 hours to 2030 hours. Each person in turn around the ward gave a talk on this or that: it could be either about themselves, history, politics or different voyages. O'Dell found this very interesting and enjoyable, and he certainly learned a lot, especially during the debates that followed some of the talks.

One of the lads in the ward who had lost a leg had played cricket for Lancashire, and he had a fund of stories. O'Dell, had liked the story about the M.C.C., where there were two entrances: one for the rich who played cricket for love, and one for those who loved cricket but could not afford to play without payment. The point of the joke was that whichever door you went through, you ended up in the same changing room. Wasn't that British snobbery at its best? Years later, on a night out in Barbados with Trueman, Lock and the polo player Williams, O'Dell asked if the two doors still existed. Their answer was unprintable.

The night it had been O'Dell's turn to give a talk, the only thing he could think of was poetry, so he had given the ward the full treatment of Rudyard Kipling, and the 'Psalm of Life' by W. W. Proctor. The presentation did not last long, and Bunts told him they all expected better next time.

At 1830 hours Bunts arrived with the Captain, who spoke first.

'As the talk tonight is one I consider to be serious, and about someone not here to defend himself, I have decided on some ground rules. First, C.P.O. Emberton will give his views as he sees them. Secondly, I myself will be the impartial adjudicator. Third, no-one will interrupt C.P.O. Emberton until he has completed his presentation and I have thrown it open to the ward for discussion.'

Then, to everyone's surprise, the interpreter joined us.

Bunts started by asking if anyone in the ward had not heard of the politician Ramsay MacDonald.

O'Dell admitted he never had. Who was he?

'Good grief,' said Bunts. 'Did they not teach you any politics at the Naval School, or at the Homes?'

'Never,' O'Dell answered defensively. 'But I learned a lot of seamanship. I can box the compass, read flags, send and receive Morse, do a shortened version of thirty-one rules of the road. And I'm considered good at maths and history.'

Bunts held up his hands.

'Sorry O'Dell. I didn't mean to embarrass you. It's just you're so naive and lack knowledge about subjects that relate to life today.'

He continued, 'Ramsay MacDonald was a great Labour leader, who truly and sincerely believed in disarmament. His battle cry was 'Disarm! Disarm! And the world will follow you!'

'MacDonald and thousands of people, very sincere people, felt the same. They were deeply and utterly committed in their belief that if we, the British, were to disarm, the world would follow.

Blair Sinclair was one of MacDonald's right hand men: so much so that Blair Sinclair went to jail for his beliefs. He organised marches and rallies with thousands of followers. Their cry was MacDonald's: 'Disarm! Disarm! The world will follow you!'.'

O'Dell listened intently as Bunts went on.

'After one particular meeting which, by the by, had been banned by the Home Office Minister, a terrible fight broke out between the disarmament camp and the police. Hundreds were injured and Sinclair went to jail. In the House of Commons Members of Parliament started to vote against strengthening the Forces, throwing ships on the scrap heap, and cancelling orders for new ones.

One aircraft carrier, six destroyers and two frigates were cancelled. The R.A.F. was cut to the bone, and half of what was left to fly was old and obsolete Gloster Gladiators and Lysanders. The Army was slimmed down by hundreds, and shells and rifles and ammunition cancelled.

All this was to cause uproar in the House of Commons. Baldwin and his camp were utterly convinced they were right: that to disarm was the only way. They called Winnie Churchill and his followers warmongers, but they, in their turn, kept pointing to Germany and Italy, who were arming themselves and getting stronger every day. Meanwhile they called MacDonald and Baldwin and their supporters 'Me Iron mongers'.

The end result was that when appeasement had to stop we were caught with our pants down. There were not enough airplanes to protect our own citizens when London, Poole, Manchester and Coventry were bombed and flattened, let alone help France.

There were not enough tanks, ammunition, guns, and rifles for our troops in France, let alone the Empire, and not enough ships to protect our coast-line, let alone the convoys and the out-posts of the Empire.

In the first two years most convoys were protected only by trawlers, armed with just a Lewis gun on the bridge and a 4.5 gun on the aft deck: hence the loss of so many ships and the men that manned them. This was also why we did a deal with the U.S.A. for fifty old three-funnel destroyers of the First War vintage.

What the Sinclairs, the MacDonalds and Baldwins of this world had to face in the end was reality: that the world is not perfect.

Now the appeaser must feel guilty for those that have died in our cities, in the outposts of the Empire, at sea and in the air, and in France, through lack of equipment, ships, soldiers and airplanes. But the appeasers held a strong sway over our nation, not the least because no sensible person wanted a sickening repeat of the horrors of the last war. Unfortunately this didn't bother Hitler.'

When Bunts had finished his lecture, the Captain stood up and said he thought C.P.O. Emberton had presented a fair assessment of the disarmament policy.

One of the lads in the ward, who turned out to be a solicitor in Civvy Street but was serving in the Merchant Navy as Radio Operator, thought that Bunts' verdict had been too simplified. As he pointed out, there had been much more to the Movement than just slogans, and also that the present Deputy Prime Minister, Clem Attlee, was a leading light in the disarmament movement. In fact, as he went on to say, it was Attlee more than Baldwin who, after MacDonald's death, fought strongly in the House of Commons for this cause. In 1935 Attlee had told the House:

'We deny the need for an increase in the Air, Arms or Navy.'

In 1937 Attlee stated in the House:

'We deny the need for an increased British Air Force or Royal Navy to make for peace in the world.'

At this point the interpreter stood up and, as she walked out of the ward, she turned at the door and said, 'In Russia we would shoot anyone who tried to leave us so vulnerable to the world.'

There was silence in the ward, everyone busy with his own thoughts. O'Dell wondered how this chap Attlee could have had the nerve to be in the British Government.

The Captain stood up and cleared his throat and said, 'Well, that is proof that we live in a democratic society. The subject is now closed. Good night all.'

O'Dell never forgot that talk. It was to have a profound impression on his future thoughts and attitude. One thing he had learnt early in life was that one could never appease a bully. He was never to forget the deaths he witnessed, nor the reason why they had no protection.

The hospital routine was by now set and regular. Everyone in the ward was getting fitter and stronger and well fed, thanks to Bunts' raids on the ships. Also they were sent a lot of heavy weather gear and crutches from Archangel, so those that could move around could visit other wards and bring back fresh news.

Around this time he was to use Miles' expression, 'sealed up' by the Russian doctor, and the tin toilet was no longer necessary. He felt embarrassed at first at asking the orderlies for the bedpan, but, like everything, he got used to it.

Miles and he were the only ones whose sores and wounds just would not heal, being full of septic pus all the time.

Later he could still recall the joy and happiness on the day he first felt the twinge of movement in his legs. It felt like a stronger version of pins and needles. His loud shout informed the ward, and in no time everyone who could move was around his bunk, as thrilled as he was. He was between tears and laughter, and kept thanking them all for the long hours they had spent rubbing and massaging his legs from the knees down.

'I'm going to walk!' he kept shouting.

Someone brought the Russian doctor and the interpreter. She told him that the doctor was very happy, and from tomorrow they would be doing a new series of exercises for him. Then the interpreter continued, 'The doctor says you will walk, but you have a long painful way to go.'

When she went on to say, 'Now we will all have a vodka,' the orderlies appeared with three bottles and they all celebrated.

The next few days were very painful: so much so that he had to keep reminding himself that once he was over the pain barrier he was going to walk.

The exercises could only be done with feet and ankles. Above the knees was still very sore with fresh eruptions around his private parts and his upper thighs. Although these parts were washed and cleaned every day they remained red and puffed and full of pus. The daily cleaning process proved very painful, and to make matters worse, as soon as he started to get the feeling back in his legs, his teeth started to drop out, and his hair started to go grey.

'I don't give a damn,' he told everyone, 'as long as I walk again.'

After all he could always get false teeth and dye his hair.

One day Miles was helping him with the bedpan because the orderlies were busy with two new arrivals in the next ward. It was a painful exercise, and when Miles noticed the perspiration breaking out on his forehead he asked, 'Do you want to rest a while O'Dell?'

'No. Let's carry on. I'll let you know when I reach the pain barrier.'

Afterwards he said to Miles 'Using that bedpan reminded me of when I was a child. It was painful then.'

'How come?' asked Miles.

'Well, if you're really interested I'll tell you.'

Just then Bunts went past.

'Hold it, O'Dell,' he said. 'Save it for tonight.'

'Oh come on, Bunts. The ward doesn't want to hear of my childhood.'

'You have only given one talk since we've been here, and that was on poetry. The ward will be very interested in a talk on your childhood, believe me,' replied Bunts.

That night at 18.30 hours he told the ward his story.

56

Chapter Six

'First of all, no matter what I tell you, you have to remember that the orphanage saved my life. I can assure you that but for the Homes I would be dead, so please take everything in perspective.

I entered the orphanage when I was just over a year old, so naturally I don't recall the details, but as my sister was eight years old at the time she does remember it, so the first part of my story is hers too.

It appears that my father was neither a very good husband nor father, and he ill-treated my mother, especially after drinking.

One night in winter when I was about three months old he returned from the pub very drunk and started into my mother, who was about five feet three inches tall and very thin. He was six feet and very big. It was, of course, no contest!

My sister said the row woke me up, and I started crying and yelling in my cot.

My drunken father then opened the door and threw my mother out into the pouring rain. He then lifted me out of the cot and threw me out too. I was lucky enough to land on my mother.

The neighbours, as my sister assured me, were all frightened of my father. They called out the police and the Orange Lodge, of which my father was a member.

I forgot to mention I was born in Belfast.

The officers of the Orange Lodge took my mother, sister and myself in for a few days. Then we returned home.

My father was taken to court and fined five shillings, but my sister told me later that on our return home there was no change in our father's attitude. A while later he de-camped (much to my mother's joy and that of the neighbours) to Glasgow, with his girlfriend.

Times were hard. There was no money coming in and no work to be had. The Orange Lodge did help out, but there were a lot of calls on their charity and there was only so much they could do.

When I was just over a year old my mother died of consumption. Although she was young by today's standards, she was worn out with ill-treatment and poverty.

The Orange Lodge had my father brought back from Glasgow under arrest to face charges of deserting his family. He was fined ten shillings by the court and immediately caught the next boat back to Glasgow.

My sister managed to hide the fact that our father had gone again, and for a while she looked after me and cared for me the best way she could. However the neighbours eventually found out, and by that time I was very ill. My sister had been raiding the neighbours' dustbins at night for scraps and soaking crusts of bread in water for me to suck.

The Orange Lodge, through the courts, got the Homes to take us in. I was immediately, with my sister, put into their hospital, dying of malnutrition, scurvy, septicaemia coursing through my blood, and covered with lice and nits. They fought a hard and long battle at the hospital, and saved my life.

Once out of hospital my sister and I transferred to the Girls' Village homes. This was, as the name suggests, only for girls, but young brothers below the age of five years were usually allowed to stay with their sisters. The Girls' Village homes were set in a beautiful village, with a number of houses (called 'cottages') positioned around a large centre area of green lawn, with lovely chestnut trees around each cottage. The Church and School were at one end and the hospital at the other.

One other thing I feel I should mention is that every Master, Matron and member of Staff employed by the Homes had, in those days, to be dedicated Christians. In most cases they were fanatically so. The Homes all over the world were run on the words:

'FEAR GOD, HONOUR THE KING AND GOD BLESS THE EMPIRE.'

Empire Day was the great day in the calendar for the Homes. The motto was drilled into us at prayers every morning and at night and the message hung on the walls of the landings outside the dormitories.

At the age of two to three years I was a sickly whining child, in and out of hospital all the time, ,covered with septic sores and running pus. (This is why I told Miles today that the bedpan brought back memories.)

I first found out I had a sister during one of my hospital periods when I woke in the hospital bed to find a girl sitting beside me. I asked her who she was, and she answered 'I am your sister.'

I said, 'What is a sister?' And while she was explaining, I fell asleep.

I have been cursed with a very retentive memory, and can remember things that happened very early on in life: so much so that my sister later on in our lives would say 'You can't possibly remember that. You were only two or three years old.'

But remember I do. One of the first things I remember is that I kept wetting the bed, and the Matron would punish me by a cold water bath; then, holding me by the ear before prayers on the landing, she got the girls to chant, 'Little boys are made of slugs and snails, and are horrid bed wetters too.' She would then declare that it was the devil in me that made me keep wetting the bed, and twisted my ear until I yelled. Then my sister would charge at the Matron who, of course, was waiting for my sister to do just that, and when my sister got near enough the Matron would slap her hard across the face, usually knocking her down. I would then try to kick the Matron in the shins, and she, in the name of the Lord, would wallop me to knock the devil out of me! To see her kneeling, a few minutes later, on the landing saying prayers, singing hymns and reading aloud the Old Testament had to be seen to be believed.

So I learned early on in life that there was something drastically wrong in what they called religion.

One day, after the usual bed wetting and punishment, my sister said to me, 'You really will have to stop this bed wetting.'

I did try hard, but matters were not helped by the dorm prefect, who belted anyone who got out of bed after lights out.

So in the end, at the age of three years, I decided to hold my penis tight at the top whenever I wanted to pass water in bed. It was extremely painful at first, but I found if I held on to the top long enough, the pain would reach a certain pitch then die away, as would the longing to pass water.

So that problem was solved.

Matron had to find another reason to pick on the O'Dells, and she was not long in doing that.

She had an obsession about drinking between meals. No matter how hot the weather, no-one was allowed to drink between meals, and of course a lot of us youngsters got thirsty playing in the sand pit.

One day I was caught drinking in the bathroom. The Matron dragged me along the passageway by my hair and, as I yelled and screamed, sure enough my sister put her head down and charged. The Matron's assistant caught hold of her and held her upside-down, while Matron delivered a few painful clouts. Then she threw me in her large cupboard. I went hysterical, screaming with fear in the dark. I don't remember being let out.

To this day I have a fear of being shut in anywhere, and cannot get in a lift, but prefer to walk up the stairs.

As usual my sister came up with the answer to the thirst problem. The school was near our cottage, and there was a drinking water tap on each side of the school. As it was part of the Village, no-one noticed if you went in the yard and drank at the water taps during the day.

One day I was running back to the house from the school yard when the Matron of the cottage next door, who was standing at their gate, spoke to me, and then gave me a sugar lump, which was to cost me dear.

As I entered the home, still licking the sugar lump (a rare treat, believe me!) I ran straight into Matron, who immediately accused me of stealing the sugar lump from our kitchen. I tried to explain, but fear and the Matron's attitude prevented me from getting the words out properly. Determined to wipe out the devil in me, shaking me and calling me a dirty little thief, matron decided my punishment should be bread and water, and the hair brush on my backside every night for a week. As a devoted Christian, Matron decided to spare me on Sunday night, but added another night on the next week to cover the seven nights.

My sister came to see me in the dormitory after my first night's punishment, and I assured her through my tears that the Matron next door had given me the sugar lump. She hugged me, and stayed with me while I lay there, hurt, frightened and angry. Although I had never heard the word 'injustice', I knew something was very wrong, and could not understand it.

On the third night of my punishment I had an experience which to this day I cannot explain.

As I was crying myself to sleep in pain and anger, I became aware of a lady resting her head on my pillow facing me. Somehow it seemed quite normal. She smiled at me, and all my pain faded away. I felt covered in a warm glow of love, and as the face slowly disappeared, I fell into sleep.

For the next four nights, after my punishment, I waited for the return of the lady, but sadly she never came.

But my pain and anger went on.

Not long after this the matron left, and a new Matron arrived.

She was wonderful, and although we still had prayers on the landing every morning and evening, and church twice on Sundays, she preached a religion of love. No hell fires, but just a deep abiding love. She kept assuring us that we were all children of God's love. If we had not had the experience of the previous Matron we might have believed her.

Everything in the Homes changed now. We were allowed to laugh, talk and run in the passageways and dorms. In the dining room we were allowed to talk while eating our meals. Bath nights became paddle nights, with much splashing of water and laughter; then, wrapped in thick warm towels, we were carried up to bed with plenty of hugs. Brothers and sisters were put into beds next to each other. Oh the joy of falling to sleep knowing my sister was in the next bed! Everyone was allowed to drink when they wanted. Dorm prefects were forbidden to hit anyone.

Another thrill was being allowed to go to the school to meet my sister as she came out, and to skip and walk back with her to the house.

Those unfortunates who wet their beds were no longer given cold baths and made to sleep in the same nightdress but were given warm baths, clean nightdresses, and hugs of encouragement to try and stop.

What a difference the new Matron made in my last year at that home!

Even Christmas Day became a day of joy, and although we only got an orange and an apple for a present, Matron got us paper hats, crackers and even nuts, which we roasted in the fire in the Common Room.

This Matron nearly convinced us that although we had no parents, God loved us and we were something precious to Jesus.

I must finish by assuring you all that I don't hold any grudge against the Homes. They fed us, educated us, and both my sister and I agree that we were far better off in the Home than anywhere else in Belfast at the time.'

There was silence in the ward when O'Dell finished.

Then the Captain, who unbeknown to him had joined them while he was talking, said, 'Well, O'Dell, your story was an eye-opener.' He continued, 'I do realise you don't believe it, but God does love all.'

He then stood up and left.

The rest of the ward all muttered various platitudes. Bunts called for lights out.

O'Dell knew, as he fell asleep, he had embarrassed them.

Chapter Seven

Not long after this Bunts arrived at his bunk.

'O'Dell,' he said, 'I have just got back from the ships. Guess what I've brought you?'

'Is it some more books?' O'Dell asked.

'Something a lot more important,' replied Bunts. 'Penicillin tablets and powder.'

O'Dell recalled reading about it in a Readers Digest.

'Do you think it will work Bunts?' he asked.

Bunts' Geordie accent only came out strong when he was excited or under stress.

'It sure will, hinny!' he answered. 'The Captain of the Yankee ship assures me it works miracles, and your septic sores, and Miles' will be healed in no time.'

The tablets caused quite a stir. The Russian doctor wanted to take the lot, but Bunts gave him half, then two days later went and asked the Captain of the American ship for some more–and got them.

How O'Dell blessed the unknown American Captain! The penicillin did work miracles. In three weeks the difference was just amazing: his sores and openings started to heal nice and clean, the puffiness and red dying away. He felt so much better in himself.

Unfortunately the same could not be said for Miles. The tablets and powder did not seem to work on him. His arm got so bad that the doctor had to amputate it. Poor Miles was so ill: he just seemed to waste away. Blood poisoning had taken over his whole body. He suffered terribly; for him the penicillin had come too late, and one night Miles passed away, seeming just to give up the fight, glad to shake off the terrible world he had found himself in at the grand old age of seventeen years.

O'Dell remembered feeling so utterly depressed, wondering who was next.

Miles was taken to Archangel, where the Russians had put a cemetery aside for foreign seamen.

Bunts returned from Archangel with more bad news: he'd been

told by the Royal Navy Padre that Leading Hand Brown had also died.

O'Dell felt in the depths of despair and for days nothing Bunts or the lads said could reach him. He just lay staring at the wood wall, not moving or even answering the Captain. He just felt enough was enough, and wallowed in self pity. He felt he could take no more, so he took no food. The orderlies had obviously dealt with the situation before, so they came regularly to lift him up and sit him on the bedpan without being asked. They kept him clean and washed.

One day Bunts came alongside his bed and said, 'O.K. O'Dell, it's time to snap out of this. Where has the gutsy fighter gone. After what you went through as a child, are you going to give up now? And what about this officer at the Naval School? Are you going to let him get away with what he did?'

He moved his head round to face Bunts.

'Oh yes,' said Bunts. 'I know all about Lieutenant Commander Yearly. Brown told me. When you were delirious on arrival here you ranted and raved about how you would deal with Yearly when you got back to the U.K. Now you're throwing in the towel and letting Yearly off. Is that it? Come on, O'Dell. I thought you had more spunk than this.'

Rage washed over him. Bunts was right: Yearly was not going to get away with what he had done. At last he spoke.

'Thanks Bunts. I had forgotten Yearly. I'll be all right now.'

Bunts patted his shoulder.

'I know you are, hinny. Just start eating.'

Around this time the Captain and some of the lads considered fit to travel were sent to Archangel to get a ship home. Two nights before he left, the Captain gave a talk on the shipping company he sailed with before the war and would be rejoining in peacetime. The company was called the World International Shipping Company, or W.I.S.C. for short. The Captain explained that it was divided into three sections:

(1) Passenger and Cruise Ships;
(2) Passenger Cargo/Cargo Ships;
(3) Tankers.

Although each section was run separately by directors. superintendents and divisional officers, the W.I.S.C. was one

Company and the sky was the limit to any employee with ambition.

'What I'm saying,' concluded the Captain, 'is should any of you wish to join the W.I.S.C. after the war, please write to me. I will endeavour to help secure you a position. Now this applies to all of you, lost limbs or not, because the Company is going to require a lot of office staff as well as seafarers.'

O'Dell's progress was becoming better and better by the day. At last he could swing his legs over the side of his bunk and, with the help of the lads or the orderlies, he gradually managed to swing himself in rhythm with the crutches. He still could not walk properly, but with his crutches and help he now managed to get to the toilet and visit other wards.

He was surprised at first to find how weak he was, but as far as he was now concerned, things could only get better.

The day came when Bunts arrived alongside his bunk.

'O'Dell, you and I and four of the lads leave a week today to join a ship at Ekonomaya, homeward bound for the U.K.!'

He was so happy to be homeward-bound at last. This seemed a funny expression on reflection, as he had no home. Still it was the U.K. he was returning to.

A week later Bunts, O'Dell and a rating joined an Empire ship, while the other three ratings joined another Empire ship astern. They were put into the ship's hospital, which was at the end of the amidships accommodation, on the starboard side.

After they had settled in they received a visit from the ship's Captain and the ship's Chief Steward. The Captain welcomed them on board; he had noticed O'Dell's crutches, and asked if he felt fit to travel.

'Oh yes Sir!'

For a horrid moment he thought the Captain was going to say he could not risk his joining the ship, but the Captain smiled and said, 'Good lad!'

Turning to Bunts, the Captain asked if he would help out on the way home with the signalling.

'I'm afraid the Navy signal is too fast for our Radio Operators,' he said.

They all laughed.

'It will be a pleasure, Sir,' said Bunts.

The Captain then went on to explain that the dockers were all Finnish prisoners of war, who had been terribly oppressed and ill-treated by the Russian guards (of whom, incidentally, 80% were women).

'You'll feel sorry for the Finns,' the Captain said. 'But under no circumstances are you to talk to them or give them anything: food, clothes, cigarettes or money. Neither must you interfere when you see the Russian guards beating them with rifle butts and boots.'

Bunts assured the Captain his orders would be carried out.

'Good!' the Captain answered. 'Because I can't emphasise enough that you will be doing the Finns no favours. If you do intervene the Russian guards are just as likely to shoot you, as well as them.'

Bunts told the Captain that he spoke Russian, and if he could be of any help at any time he was at the Captain's service. In a bitter voice the Captain made a peculiar remark.

'I only hope, C.P.O., that there are some Germans left at the end of the war for when we fight these Russian bastards.'

With that parting shot he left.

The Chief Steward (Catering Officer) then introduced himself, and explained they would be expected to look after themselves, collect their meals, draw their rations, cutlery, dry stores etcetera from the Second Steward. They had to keep the hospital clean and tidy at all times. Bunts assured the Chief Steward the ratings would see to that. Chief Steward then went on to explain that not only was he the ship's caterer, but he was also in charge of the hospital and all medical treatment, from treating V.D. to pulling out teeth, dressing wounds, boils, strapping up broken legs: all this on a Red Cross certificate! Then he left them to settle in.

Bunts sent the rating, James Clark (Nobby of course) to draw the rations while he went off to make up the number with the D.E.M.S. gunners.

Because there was snow and ice on the deck, Bunts ordered O'Dell to stay in the hospital until Nobby or he returned.

The standard of living on board the ship was an eye-opener. Apart from the fact there was hot and cold water on tap and one could turn electric lights off and on as required, the food issue was first class. It seemed the ship had deep freezes that held frozen beef, pork, lamb and fish for four months. and large dry storerooms also capable of holding four months supply of dry stores. There were Dunlop mattresses, white sheets and pillow cases for everyone. A tin of condensed milk only had to last a week, and there were plenty of eggs, bacon and cereals for everyone, not just officers. It was a far cry from the *S.S. Llandudno.*

The biggest shock of the day was yet to come. The night shift dockers were marched down to the docks, four abreast. There seemed to be hundreds of them relieving the day shift. Their clothing, footwear and headgear, was pitiful to behold in that terrible frozen waste. Most had wrapped themselves up in sacks, tarpaulins and cardboard; around their feet were parts of shoes and boots, also wrapped in sacking and tied up by string.

It was a terrible sight. The Russian guards shouted and screamed at them and used their rifle butts, boots and fists savagely. 'This was Man's inhumanity to Man' expressed at its worst.

Later O'Dell could still recall how horrified he had felt, and had found it hard to reconcile the warm compassionate Russian doctors, nurses and interpreters with these mad screaming guards. He spoke about it to Bunts, who smiled and said, 'Everything seems black or white when you're young, O'Dell. But in a mature world there are a lot of shades of grey, as you will find out as you get older.'

But for once Bunts was wrong; for O'Dell life would always be black or white. Good or bad, the word 'compromise' was to be utterly repugnant to him all his life. It was to cost him friends, promotion and cause him hard times in the years to come, but he never, ever compromised.

That night the D.E.M.S. gunners came to see Bunts. They told awful stories about the treatment of the Finnish P.O.W.s. They said if they looked on the ice on the portside, they would see a mound of ice and snow: there lay a Finnish P.O.W. His crime had been that he was caught with some bread the cook had given him. The Russian guards had belted the cook, then taken the poor P.O.W. down on the ice via the rope ladder, stripped him and forced him to sit on the ice, where he stayed until he died. All work was stopped on the ships while the P.O.W.'s were made to face the ice, watching their compatriot die.

They were then told this was the punishment for anyone found with ship's food.

The next day, when the shift marched and shuffled down, O'Dell took a good look at the Finns: their eyes and faces were dull, dead and utterly resigned. They were like walking zombies, as if death would be a release from a living hell. Yet they must have had some spark of life left: some of the female P.O.W.s had babies with them and these babies must have been born in the camp.

All four ships were tied up starboard side on. It was so cold that once the ships got alongside, they became frozen in, the ice reaching three to four feet in depth after a week or two. All ships had to keep their propellers turning over slowly, but even so at the average of twenty below, just three feet from the ship's propellers there was thick ice.

The last day of discharging arrived. It was to be a day of utter calamity for the poor Finnish P.O.W.'s.

At number four hatch, which was right outside the hospital, the P.O.W.'s were busy discharging a Bren gun carrier up and out of the hatch, when one of the clutch brakes on one of the four winches slipped, then broke. The carrier tipped up, and before anyone could stop it smashed on the one below.

The Russian guards went demented, screaming and yelling. They took the four winchmen to the gangway, belting them with rifle butts and boots. In vain the Chief Officer and the Third Engineer Officer Norman, tried to explain that the clutch plate was worn out and that it was not sabotage. But to no avail. Bunts was called by the Captain to explain in Russian, but no matter what anyone said, the Russians were convinced the incident was due to sabotage. Even after the Third Engineer Officer had shown them the worn out clutch plate and repaired the winch, nothing, but nothing would convince the guards that it was not sabotage. They even turned on the Engineer Officer and accused him of covering up the sabotage and threatened to take him ashore with the winchmen.

The four Finns were taken ashore and shot.

As the night shift dockers shuffled on to the docks and the day shift went off they all had to pass the four dead winchmen laid out under the lights at the dock gates. A loud speaker informed them, 'This is what happens to all saboteurs.'

It shook everyone on board. The ship's Captain, who hailed from Glasgow, called them animals, but that night, in the hospital, Bunts said he thought that remark was an insult to animals.

Two days later the ice breaker *Lenin* arrived. As it broke up ice around the ships O'Dell watched the mound turn over.

Freed at last from the land, the ship seemed to come alive, swinging itself in line behind the other ships and following the ice breaker through the ice flows out to the clear sea, heading for the Kola Bay at Murmansk.

Three days later, and after four heavy air raids, they left Kola Bay and headed for the open sea, for Iceland then the U.K.

The passage home was a lot easier than the passage outward. Apart from two U-boat attacks and the loss of three ships, the fog, then near-hurricane weather day after day kept the German Air Force and U-boats at bay. The weather was truly appalling: the ships, being in ballast, were being thrown all over the place. Bunts reported the ships were finding it near impossible to keep station. He swore he had actually seen the keel of one of the merchant ships. Although everyone cursed and groaned and found sleep impossible, they all knew in their hearts that they were at least safe from attacks.

Bunts and Nobby put up the sides of the hospital bed, and another mattress sideways on in the bed, so that O'Dell would not be thrown out and his wounds re-opened.

Three weeks later they anchored off Iceland in a blinding snow storm, to join an awaiting convoy for the last lap home. O'Dell remembered for a long time afterwards how he had, with Nobby's help, swung himself into the hospital and saw Bunts sitting in his chair looking fast asleep. He shouted 'Bunts! Bunts! We have anchored!' But Bunts did not move. All of a sudden he had that awful feeling. Nobby moved in front of him, went up to Bunts, knelt down and lifted his head, then, turning towards O'Dell said, 'Sorry O'Dell. He is dead.'

Everything was a haze after that. He recalled screaming, 'No! No!' Then Nobby put him to bed.

The Captain, Chief Officer and Chief Steward arrived shortly after and Bunts was taken away. O'Dell heard Nobby telling the Captain,

'Bunts treated O'Dell like a son. In fact, once O'Dell was cleared by the doctors. Bunts was going to offer him a home.'

'Oh Bunts!' he thought. 'You never told me that wonderful news, and now you never will.'

He swore to himself that no one would ever get close to him again, yet that night, and for a long time after, he had felt heartsick, and in the darkness of the night he cried tears of pain. He had let Bunts get under his guard, and felt his loss deeply.

To him there was no rhyme or reason why this wonderful caring man had been recalled to colours at fifty six years old, after going through so much and doing so much for others. Why should he die on the last lap home? Where was this marvellous God? Where was justice?

The Captain came the next day, and explained that C.P.O. Emberton had died from a heart attack. His body had been taken shore side, but he felt, with the ship at anchor and O'Dell still on crutches, it would not be safe to attempt going down a steep floating gangway to attend the funeral.

Next day the Captain, Chief Officer, Chief Engineer Officer, Chief Steward, Chief Radio Operator and all the D.E.M.S. gunners, in their number one uniforms, went ashore and Bunts was buried with full military honours.

Everyone on the ship was very kind, but O'Dell felt numb, and was so glad when they eventually sailed, and they arrived safely in Hull.

The R.T.O. officer came on board and asked him where he lived, as they liked to send those wounded to the nearest military hospital near their families and friends.

He answered that anywhere in Durham would do. So they decided to send him to the Ingham Infirmary.

He was met at Newcastle-on-Tyne station by a C.P.O. from the R.T.O. office, accompanied by two Wrens, who had brought a Royal Navy van to drive him to the Infirmary. The C.P.O. pulled his leg and said, 'Who's the lucky one then? Two Wrens as soon as he arrived home!'

On arrival at the Infirmary, he was examined by doctors, given a hot bath, a meal, then allotted a bed. As he sank into the bed, with its crisp white sheets, an army nurse bent over him and asked about his next of kin: he knew his voyage to Russia was over and he drifted off to sleep.

He felt someone pulling at his shoulder. Why wouldn't they let him sleep? He heard a voice penetrating through his sleep, asking him:

'Are you all right sir? Are you all right sir?'

He opened his eyes. A young, police officer was bending over him, looking very concerned.

He thought, 'A police officer - what is he doing here?'

For a moment or two he felt completely disorientated; opening his eyes again it all flooded back. Of course, he was in Liverpool.

Again he heard the policeman ask if he was all right.

Slightly dazed, he replied 'Oh yes, thank you Officer. I must have fallen asleep.'

'Not a pastime I would recommend around here!' said the policeman, sitting down next to him.

He explained he had been to the Russian Consulate, then had walked to the Pier Head and fallen asleep.

He looked at his watch.

'Oh dear! I've missed my train. I must phone home.'

He stood up, stamping his feet, and clapping his hands.

'Gosh, I'm cold! No wonder I was dreaming I was back in Russia.'

The police officer was kindness itself.

'Well, sir,' he said, standing up. 'I'm going up town towards the station. It would be a pleasure to keep you company. It's not often one meets someone just honoured by the Russians.'

Chapter Eight

The police officer kept him company until they reached the station. O'Dell thanked the officer for looking after him, they shook hands, and the officer continued on his way.

In the station booking office he found there would not be another train to his destination for an hour. He telephoned home to let his wife Betty know he had missed the train, and would be late.

While waiting for the train he noticed a large poster advertising the North Wales resort of Llandudno. The name brought back memories of his first ship, *S.S. Llandudno*.

What a ship! What a voyage! Although he was to stay at sea for thirty five years, no voyage ever took the place of the first. There was no doubt in his mind that, war apart, the first voyage was his happiest.

The train eventually arrived. He got into the compartment and sank thankfully into his seat. It had been a long day; he was cold and tired; he would be glad to reach home.

As the train pulled out slowly from the station, another poster of Llandudno caught his eye. He thought to himself that the dear old *Llandudno* had been a happy ship. The train slowly lulled him to sleep, as he drifted once again into the past.

He had been sent by the orphanage to Cardiff, there to try to join a ship. He knew the people at the H.Q. of the Homes could not make him out: only a few months ago he had left the Naval School, saying he did not want to go to sea and now he was pestering them for a merchant ship.

The Home at Cardiff was really just a transit house for those trying to get to sea, and those who wanted to stay there after a voyage. At the time the Government, Shipping Officer, B.O.T., and the Seamen's Union were trying to start up a pool system to which all Merchant Navy personnel reported at the end of their leave to apply for their next ship. It was a good thing from everyone's point of view, especially that of the Unions, as it meant everyone joining a ship had to pay union dues–something a lot of seamen objected to. This had not yet taken over officially, and a lot of Captains still liked to pick their own crews from among seamen tramping the docks looking for a berth.

After tramping the docks for three days and not having any success, on the fourth morning O'Dell came across the old *S.S. Llandudno*; and old she certainly was, having been built in 1912. She was filthy, having just come from the coaling staiths. Coal dust was thick everywhere.

He went on board and someone pointed out the Captain, who was talking on the wing of the bridge, port side.

As he walked forward he passed a boy about his own age and he asked him if there were any jobs going. The young boy, who turned out to be a deck apprentice, smiled and said, 'You'll have to go up and ask him,' pointing to the Captain.

When he reached the bridge, O'Dell stood there, feeling embarrassed and unsure of what to do.

The Captain turned to him and said, in a beautiful Welsh lilt, 'What do you want, boyo?'

O'Dell sprang to attention and stammered 'A job Sir.'

The Captain looked him up and down and said, 'What the hell are you bach? A bloody sea cadet?'

'No Sir. Naval training ship.'

'Well I'm sorry boyo, but there is no job here.'

O'Dell turned away feeling disappointed, and left the bridge, heading for the gangway aft. Just as he reached the gangway a voice which also had a lovely Welsh accent said, 'Would you be looking for work bach?'

He turned. The speaker was a scruffy looking man covered in coal dust and oil, but he saw the epaulettes with four gold bars and automatically sprang to attention.

'Yes Sir.'

The speaker waved his hand.

'Well, boyo, cut out that bull shit and follow me.'

O'Dell blushed as he heard the dockers and others tittering. He could now see the purple between the gold bars and realised the officer he was following was the ship's Chief Engineer, who took him into a wide alleyway between the accommodation and the engine room casing, the accommodation and engineers' saloon being right up to the ship's side, port side on, with the alleyway open at both ends. He had climbed up out of the well deck, up the companionway then up along the boat deck to the bridge when he came on board, so he'd missed the open alleyway.

With a grunt of, 'Mind the high storm step boyo,' the Chief abruptly turned half-way along the alleyway and stepped into a room; or to be more precise into the Engineers' Saloon.

Two things struck O'Dell right away: the beautiful panelling of oak and rosewood all around the saloon, and the stove or bogie on the left as they stepped in. Somehow he'd never thought that ships still had coal-burning fires.

There was a table in the centre with seating for six. At this table sat three men in filthy overalls covered with coal, oil and grease. They turned out to be the Second, Third and Fourth Engineer Officers–all Welshmen. The Chief introduced O'Dell as a boy looking for work and they all said, 'Bara Da.' The Chief said, 'Oh, he's English,' and they smiled and said, 'Welcome,' in their Welsh lilt.

There was a comfortable looking old settee running fore and aft along the bulkhead (wall). It had obviously seen better days, and was in need of a darned good polish and new upholstery.

There were two doors each end inside the saloon. One on the portside just inside the saloon led to the Chief Engineer's cabin; on the starboard side, facing forward, the door led to the engineer's pantry, which, like the saloon, was filthy with dirt and coal dust.

He found out later that the ship had been in port for six weeks and never once in that period had the Engineers' accommodation, saloon, toilets or pantry been cleaned out.

The chief took him into the pantry and switched on the light. Immediately the bulkheads became whiter and seemed to move. What he had taken for coal dust on the bulkheads turned out to be literally hundreds of crawling cockroaches

'Not frightened of a few insects are you bach?' Asked the Chief.

O'Dell shot to attention. 'No Sir!'

'All right! All right! Cut that out,' said the Chief. This is Merchant Navy, not R.N. We don't need that bull.'

The Chief then took him forward to where the Captain was still on the wing of the bridge. The Chief shouted up to him.

'This lad is signing on as Mess Boy. What time do you want him at the shipping office?'

The Captain shouted back, 'Eleven hundred hours tomorrow morning.'

Then the Chief took O'Dell to the Chief Steward and told him, 'This lad is signing on as our Mess Boy tomorrow.'

The Chief Steward had two wavy gold braid bands on his epaulettes and at first O'Dell thought him to be R.N.R., until he noticed the gold braid was sharp zig-zag, not the smooth wave of R.N.R. The Chief Steward welcomed him, and told him to come and collect his bedding issue and working gear once he had signed on.

Then the Chief Engineer said, 'Right, boyo. Off you go. See you tomorrow.'

O'Dell rushed back to the Home to tell the House Master that he had a job.

When the House Master heard the name of the ship he said, 'Good grief! That has got to be one of the hardest shipping companies in the world. No-one joins their ships unless they are desperate.'

O'Dell replied, 'It's what I want. It's a job.' The House Master had been shipping boys out to sea for years. He realised that O'Dell meant what he said and gave him every support, but at the same time pointing out that the reason the Homes' H.Q. had sent him out in his Naval School uniform was in the hope that he would get a deck job.

The Master helped him pack his kit bag, which was the Homes' standard blue one with his name and number 109 still on it, and also found him a small brown suitcase. Into this case the Master put two old blue bed sheets and pillow cases, as well as cleaning rags, Ronuk and Brasso.

'If it's as filthy as you say, that company is too mean to supply you with enough cleaning gear, but they certainly don't supply bedsheets and pillow cases.'

That night O'Dell could not sleep. His whole body was alive and tingling with excitement. He was going to sea! All he could think of over and over again was he was off to sea.

Eventually he got up, left the dormitory and went down to the kitchen and made a cup of tea. As he was sitting there, drinking and trying to quiet his racing mind, the Master arrived to join him. He smiled. 'Thought it would be you, O'Dell. You can't sleep for excitement–am I right?'

'I'm so excited I can't sleep,' O'Dell agreed.

The Master talked to him about the ship and the shipping company and then put him wise to one or two things O'Dell was to find useful at sea.

'O'Dell, I've read your file and what I and the H.Q. can't fathom out is why, after all your effort to join the Naval School, you wanted to opt out. After all, your progress report from the Naval School is nothing but complimentary. You seem to have done so well in signals, seamanship, and you made first team football, won two medals boxing and got top marks in the display team. It seems such a shame you didn't carry on and enter the R.N. as Boy Seaman.

You don't have to explain to me, O'Dell, if you'd rather not, but I can assure you if you do I will respect your confidence in not repeating what you tell me.'

O'Dell thought for a moment, then he said, 'Well, Master, you have been more than kind to tell you, and to be honest I don't mind who you tell. It's all behind me now. I'm free and off to sea!'

He arrived at the Naval School in December 1938, having travelled down with three other lads from different Homes who also wanted to go to sea. They were met at the station by a Petty Officer, who took over the escort from the Homes. When the P.O. saw O'Dell, he smiled and said, 'So you made it, Titch.'

'Yes, Sir,' he replied.

'First thing to learn, Titch, you never call anyone except an officer 'Sir'. All others you call by their rank. For example me you call Petty Officer. A Killock, or one anchor man, you call Leading Hand, and you never speak to someone of senior rank until they speak to you. And you always, and I mean ALWAYS, stand to attention when answering. Do I make myself clear?'

O'Dell sprang to attention.

'Yes, Petty Officer.'

Turning to the other three lads, the P.O. asked them their names; each sprang to attention as they answered. There was nothing new in this. In every Home no-one spoke until a Master or Matron spoke first. Once they said, 'What is it boy?' or called them by number, 'What is it number 109?' they stood to attention, and when finished they took a pace back, about turned, and then marched off.

The P.O. then said that he knew Titch because at the last Empire Day each Home and the two Naval Schools had sent a selection of boys and girls to B.G.C. so that the Homes could celebrate Empire Day and the Coronation in one big jubilee.

'Titch here pestered the life out of me for four whole days on how to get into the Naval School, asking what was life like in the School. Well,' continued the P.O., 'he, like you three, will find out the hard way.'

Calling them to attention with their standard blue kitbags slung over their shoulders, the P.O. marched them from the station to Naval School. Just before they arrived at the entrance the P.O. halted them, telling them to stand at ease, with kitbags resting at their feet. Once they had got their breath back the P.O. said, 'Right. This is what we are going to do. We're going to march in very smartly. On entering I'll call out 'eyes right', the two on duty Quartermasters will present arms, the O.O.D. (Officer of the Day) will salute, then I will call 'eyes front', and you will keep marching until I call a halt. Is that clear?'

They hastened to assure the P.O. that it was quite clear.

As they marched in O'Dell felt so proud, and lucky. At last he had made the Naval School and for the first time since leaving Suffolk he felt a twinge of happiness.

The P.O. called, 'Eyes right!'

The officer saluted, the two Q.M.s presented arms, and O'Dell felt six feet tall.

The P.O. called, 'Eyes front, then halt!'

The officer moved over to look them up and down, then said, 'Carry on P.O.'

The entrance to the Naval School was very impressive. Just inside on the portside, two large six foot crossed stone anchors were painted a brilliant white. A hundred yards further on was a mast, with yard-arms out-spread. This mast was a hundred and twenty feet high, and every boy had to climb it once a month.

O'Dell was eventually allocated a berth in Howard House, and fitted out with his uniforms: working rig, school rig, and number one best rig for Sunday and other special day parades. How thrilled he was to get into uniform, but of course he didn't show it.

The Naval School was laid out like a ship, and was always referred to as a ship. The bows, or forecastle, were a large house where the older boys lived. The buildings were called the Nauticals, the Lower Playing fields, the Chief Officer's house and the Gymnasium.

The large feeding hall, called Jellicoe Hall, was the mess deck. The quarter deck was Captain's quarters, and included the administration office, mast and the two crossed anchors.

Portside was the Secondary School, and lifeboats were housed upon a six foot high platform, so that there could be practising of lowering, then heaving back up to swing in on their davits.

Starboard side consisted of three large houses, and the Naval Chapel, with the upper playing fields and the site where there would be air raid shelters. Stern or aft consisted of hospital, swimming pool and the seamanship school.

Amidship was a large oblong parade ground—at least it appeared large to a young boy's eyes.

In the harbour was a whaler, and one lifeboat for practising rowing and sailing.

Each house held between forty and fifty boys.

It was tradition that every new boy was called a Mush and a senior boy was always appointed to look after the Mush for three weeks, after which the Mush was on his own. Apart from the fact that the senior boy had to show the Mush what, where and how things were done and not done, he had to make sure none of the boys picked a fight with the new Mush until the three weeks were up.

It was woe betide any boy caught breaking this rule. The punishment for breaking it and being caught was to run the gauntlet of wet knitted towels wheeled by the other boys in the dormitory while the guilty boy was completely naked, or to be carried to the top playing fields naked and thrown into the gorse bushes.

Like all the other Homes there was a pecking order relating to where you stood in relationship to other boys in this 'survival of the fittest' world. In three weeks a new Mush could usually work out where he stood in the pecking order, and the boys soon put his theory to the test. A new Mush usually had at least three or four fights before his position in the pecking order in both his house and ship was finalised.

The Masters and Matrons in the Homes allowed for a settling

down period, as did the officers, teachers and Matrons in the Naval School.

O'Dell found it hard at first to get the hang of what the bugle calls meant, but he soon learnt. He took to the Naval School like a duck to water. Each day that passed he enjoyed more and more. He enjoyed the hard but fair discipline, the schools, all the sports and the one hour daily work out in the gym, where he could box, wrestle, do matwork, parallel bars work, weight lifting, or work on the horse box, under the supervision of a wonderful P.T. Officer V. Curtis.

The food, like that in the Homes, was good and adequate, but of course everyone moaned and groused about it. It never ceased to amaze him how well-fed, clothed and housed they were when he considered it was all run on charity.

There was only a small number of sadists and perverts that slipped through the staff selection procedure and made life unhappy, but for every bad one there were five good. It has to be said though that the bad were really bad, and the good normal ones never ever attempted to stop them.

By the time his three weeks were up, O'Dell was set into the routine and enjoying it. Prayers first thing on the landing was still first order of the day God, King and Empire, plus the Navy thrown in. After prayers it was into working gear; the dormitory, landing, passageways, playrooms, bathroom, toilets and the open yard at the back were all cleaned and polished, ready for inspection.

Then came bugle call to wash and change into school rig. the second bugle called to march down to breakfast in Jellicoe Hall. Once in position at the house table, everyone stood to attention until Glazebrook, the Purser, ordered everyone to face aft and recite the motto on the bulkhead, which was written in two-foot letters:

WHEN THE GREAT SCORER COMES TO WRITE AGAINST YOUR NAME HE WILL WRITE NOT HOW YOU WON OR LOST, BUT HOW YOU PLAYED THE GAME.

Everyone then faced inwards to their seat, and after a long blow on the whistle, everyone sat down and ate in complete silence. Then prayers again, this time in Jellicoe Hall, led by the Captain who was pukka R.N.

Ordinary school work followed until midday.

After midday dinner in the mess hall the afternoon was devoted to seamanship, and one hour gym work. In spring and summer there was football and cricket in the evenings.

When O'Dell had been there about two weeks, he thought out what to do about the pecking order.

In their dormitory at Howard House was the house bully, McFay: a big-mouth, always shouting at, and clipping the ears of juniors. O'Dell had already shown his contempt of the big bully whenever they met by his scornful looks, and he had heard that the bully was telling his mates what he was going to do to 'that new Mush', soon as the three weeks were up.

The night after the three weeks were up, the bully started again in the dormitory after lights out.

With his heart racing and palms sweating O'Dell decided this was IT, and in a loud voice he said, 'Why don't you shut up and let us sleep, big mouth?'

There was complete silence in the dormitory.

McFay asked, 'Who said that?'

There was a chorus of, 'O'Dell the new Mush!'

O'Dell shot out of bed and waited in the middle of the dormitory.

Big Mouth said 'It's a good job you're a Mush.'

'Don't let that worry you. I ceased being a Mush yesterday,' said O'Dell.

McFay got out of bed, making for the middle of the dormitory.

A voice said, 'Hold it!' It was Leading Hand Brown. 'Now, before you two start anything I want to know if you are aware of what you are doing, O'Dell. McFay is about two years older and at least a stone and a half heavier than you.'

O'Dell assured L.H. Brown he was aware of those facts.

'O.K.,' said L.H. Brown, 'but don't forget the rules. No holding, no knees, no head butts and no feet, and when one goes down the other waits until he is up. And when I say stop, it stops.'

Gritting his teeth, O'Dell went at McFay hammer and tongs, and to his surprise he went down. Stepping back, he let McFay get up. This time the bully was ready, and although O'Dell kept to his 'mind over pain' attitude, McFay hurt him and knocked him down. As O'Dell got to his feet he could see he had split the bully's lip and cut over his right eye. But O'Dell knew he was in a mess and he went down again. After McFay had knocked him down again, the bully said, 'Have you had enough O'Dell?'

O'Dell knew that if his theory was to work he had to stay with it, so climbing to his feet he said, 'You've got to be kidding' and threw himself at his opponent.

Like all bullies, McFay was getting worried. Not only was he running out of breath, but the more he hit O'Dell, the more O'Dell came back at him. It was true that after the first attack the younger boy had not hurt him much, but O'Dell had got a few hard blows in and McFay didn't like them.

After knocking O'Dell down again, McFay appealed to L.H. Brown, so that in the eyes of the dormitory although O'Dell was getting a hiding it was McFay who wanted to quit.

L.H. Brown said, 'Right, you two. That's enough. Shake hands.'

O'Dell protested he still wanted to fight, when in truth it was the last thing he wanted!

L.H. Brown said sharply, 'That's enough, O'Dell. Go and get washed and cleaned up, then report to me.'

Once washed and cleaned up, O'Dell reported to L.H. Brown, with McFay. This time they shook hands, but O'Dell looked McFay in the eye and told the bully he would have another go any time he wanted.

O'Dell knew by the look in McFay's eyes there would not be another fight. Like all bullies, he was frightened because he couldn't understand how O'Dell kept coming back for more and had shown no sign of pain.

McFay didn't know that years before, after the sugar lump episode in the Home, O'Dell had decided to rise above the pain barrier whenever he could. At Suffolk and the Boys' city he had held burning matches under his fingers, blistering and burning them, without showing pain.

O'Dell's plan worked. The next day tales of the fight were all over the ship, and the fight did not lack enlargement as the versions travelled from House to House.

Chapter Nine

He became a five days' wonder: all the boys, big and small, came to look at him. It was decided that I must be slightly mad if I didn't have the sense to know when I was beaten, so my wish came true and for the rest of my time in the Naval School I had a fairly peaceful time, and my slot in the pecking order was established.

I settled down to an enjoyable life in Howard House, and I liked Saturday mornings with square bashing, fire drill and mast climbing. But Sunday to me was the great day. Of course it didn't pay to show it, and I moaned as much as everyone else, but Sunday morning parade, after church, never ceased to thrill me, watching the flag unfurl, the Captain standing on the raised dais, saluting us as we marched past, the band blaring out a full-throated military tune. We felt Britain was awake, and all was right with the world. I felt I would have gladly laid down my life for God, King and Empire.

I was to find my retentive memory a great help, and soon learnt the Morse Code. I could send and receive with the best the international flags and semaphore, and even a shortened version of Seafarers Rules of the Road proved no problem.

One of the first things I did on joining the Naval School was to put my name down to join the band. In due course I was allowed to join the practice sessions for bugle and drums. Eventually I became a full member of the band as a bugler. It was a marvellous band, consisting of fourteen buglers, sixteen fifes, six kettle drums and eight side drums and one bass drum. The noise we made was incredible, drowning out all opposition wherever we met it, be it Scouts, Air Cadets, Army Cadets, and even the local Salvation Army.

I had been at the ship about three months when I discovered that I actually feared water, or at least deep water. I came to dread swimming lessons, which started every spring under the watchful eye of the Seamanship Officer. Every boy had to pass out in swimming or leave the Naval School. By gritting my teeth I forced myself to do the breast stroke, back stroke and diving.

The day eventually came when I had to pass out. The swimming exam was three lengths of breast stroke, one of back stroke, one swallow dive, followed by floating on the water.

Fearfully I did the required three lengths of breast stroke, one of back stroke, but then came the really hard part for me the swallow dive from the high dive board. Then came floating until a P.O. swam under me to see I hadn't a foot on the bottom.

How I got through it I'll never know: my whole body cringed inside with fear. But I did.

Once this exam was passed we never had to attend swimming again unless we wished to. I never went near that pool again, and in all my years at sea I never conquered my fear of deep water.

Life in the ship carried on. There was a lot of talk about war. The officers assured us there would be war, despite that old grey man coming back from Munich, waving a piece of paper.

Once the air raid shelters on the top playing fields were complete, we started air raid practices. Being young we actually enjoyed these.

I enjoyed a brief period of notoriety when it became known that in 1938 I had met and talked with young Germans of the Hitler Youth. Everyone wanted to know how they dressed, how they swaggered when marching with their dirks in their belts with a swastika in the handle of the dirk. They could all speak English, were arrogant beyond belief, and, like our officers, were sure there would be another war which this time they would win.

A Sunday morning came when we marched on Parade after church to hear the Captain announce that we were at war with Germany. It was 3rd September 1939.

The Captain said he expected everyone to do his duty, to remember that he wore the uniform of the greatest Navy in the world, the Senior Service. We would never lay down our arms until once again the Hun was beaten. He went on to say that tradition would be upheld, and Retreat would not be played again by the band on the quarter deck each evening, as had been the practice, until the war was over.

The Navy never plays Retreat in wartime, but our Captain assured us it would be played loud and clear on Victory Day.

Then it was hats off, and three cheers for King and Country.

We young lads went wild with joy: at last we would give Hitler a punch in the nose.

Two hours later we had our first air raid, then the All Clear sounded an hour later.

Only our Matron didn't seem happy. That night at prayers on the landing she had tears in her eyes as she asked God to take care of us and for the war to end soon. We thought she was a spoil sport. We didn't want it to end until we had a crack at the Hun.

1939 was a very good year for me: I even won the best set of teeth award when two dentists went through all two hundred boys and I scooped the award. Who would have dreamt then that just over two years later my teeth would all fall out and my hair would turn grey.

Although I studied hard and would recite to myself for hours, even after lights out, it was not all hard slog. There was plenty of sport which I enjoyed greatly; my health improved, but although my neck, shoulder, arms and leg muscles became big and firm, I still didn't grow any taller and couldn't throw off the name of 'Titch'.

The officers were fair but hard; they had no time for any boy that whined or couldn't take the discipline. Their contempt for any boy that actually erred was utter and complete. The school teachers were also hard but fair, except for one–the Head Teacher who incidentally, held R.N.R. rank. His name was Yearly, and every boy and teacher feared him. He was a sadistic bastard. I decided very early to stay well clear of Lieutenant Commander Yearly R.N.R. I knew from my gut feelings and experiences in other Homes that he was the type I feared and loathed.

The Matrons (all called 'Gussies' behind their backs) were also fair but hard, but from what the other boys said, we in Howard House were lucky. Our Matron only slapped us hard across the face before putting us on defaulters. Other Matrons, it seemed, used the cane or broom stick.

Christmas came and went. We got the usual orange and apple, otherwise the Phony War, as it was called at this time, carried on. We had a lot of air raids and we liked to pretend the German Air Force was trying to wipe out the Naval School, but in reality we knew they were trying to wipe out the sea plane base and Sunderland flying boats, which were at anchor in the harbour.

In April 1940 I passed out in signals. I felt so proud when the Captain pinned the badge of cross flags on my arm on Sunday parade.

On May 27th 1940 the Naval School received a request for a signal team to man the signal station in the harbour. Although we didn't know it at the time, it was to free the men manning the station so that they could be sent to help get our lads off the beach at Dunkirk.

I couldn't believe my luck when I was selected, with seven others and one P.O. for this job. It was so exciting and we all felt six feet tall, sending out messages to real Navy ships and lamping their orders to them.

Unfortunately some of the Senior Nauticals felt they should have been picked and showed their displeasure when we arrived back. We two juniors were accused of being the Signal Officer's pets: this was rich, seeing that only two weeks before going to the signal station the Signal Officer had given me six of the best with his thick strap on the grounds of silent insubordination. His charge was that my eyes spoke while my mouth was shut: after the flogging I'd not been able to sit down comfortably for a week!

The hassle and harassment carried on for a couple of days, especially from one particular Senior Nautical. In the end I saw red, my fuse blew and I went for him. I was so furious that I didn't remember much of the fight later on, but I was told afterwards that it was a humdinger! As I came out of my red tunnel of rage, who should be holding me by the collar of my Navy jersey but Lieutenant Commander Yearly. He was shaking me very hard then, as he let go, I fell and he kicked me, shouting, 'On your feet! Attention!' I got to my feet and glared at him. He promptly slapped me hard across my face and hit me in the stomach as I went down again.

I got back on my feet to attention to hear Yearly shouting that he had seen me attack the Senior Nautical. My punishment was to be escorted to the gymnasium and put in the ring with the Senior Nautical for three rounds. As we entered the gym, Yearly ordered the P.T. Officer to referee and said that all the boys that wanted to could come in and watch. As you can imagine, every boy that could get there came.

Half an hour later, when the fight started, two lads from my dormitory acted as my seconds, despite knowing that they would be marked down by Yearly for it. I knew I could box at my weight and age and win, but I was no match for a Senior, who was even older and heavier than McFay!

You can't afford to lose your temper in the ring. I got another good hiding, but by keeping my gloves well up and doing my mind over pain routine I managed to survive three rounds, but lost easily on points. However I felt the Senior knew he had been in a fight and in the last round he went a little easy on me.

My reputation was confirmed as slightly mad and no-one tangled with me after June 1940. Except Yearly.

Both P.O. Gower and the P.T. Officer warned me to stay out of Yearly's way as much as possible, which I did. Every boy knew Yearly had marked me out, so they tended to shy away from me, but I was a loner anyway so it didn't bother me too much and I still enjoyed everything else about the ship.

Then Yearly started to visit classes I was in, telling the teacher to carry on and he would sit, looking at me with a sneer on his face. It was very unnerving: I forced myself to show nothing of my feelings either in my eyes or manner. Then Yearly would just get up and walk out of the class.

I was conscious of the other boys' sympathy for me and I hated that.

Life carried on.

One day while we were playing football on the upper playing fields, Yearly found one of the boys playing in the air raid shelter, against strict orders.

All football stopped and the two teams, along with the Referee Officer and two P.O. linesmen, watched as Yearly beat the hell out of the junior seaman with his heavy stick as the boy lay on the deck.

Then a voice was heard shouting, 'Stop that you bully! Stop that at once!'

It was a woman's voice, then a man's voice shouted, 'Come over this hedge and hit someone your own size you bastard!' This turned out to be the woman's husband.

The man tried to get through the hedge to get to Yearly and was threatened with gaol for trespassing.

All hands were ordered off the upper playing fields and down to the Parade Ground.

The couple went to the police, who called on the Captain and Yearly. What was said during the interview no boy ever found out. As the police officer left, escorted by Yearly, he was heard by the two Quartermasters to say, 'I completely understand, Sir. Discipline must be maintained. I'm an ex-service man myself and I'm sorry to have troubled a fine officer like yourself.'

The police officer didn't even ask to see the boy to examine the bruises on his neck, back and legs.

Around this time I had been moved to a bed just inside the door of the dormitory. Leading Hand Brown was in the bed opposite me; one of the jobs I'd been detailed was to give out blankets - one to each boy as they ran to the air raid shelter in the dark at night. The blankets were stored under my bed and my duty was to give them out until there was only one left, which would be mine, then to report to Leading Hand Brown that the dormitory was empty. We did this every real and practice raid until we became very good at running in the dark to the shelters.

One day, out of the blue, my sister arrived. She had joined the A.T.S. and was on embarkation leave. All the boys, including me, thought she was beautiful: she had lovely ash blond hair and a most beautiful smile.

My sister was allowed to take me out of the Naval School for three hours. I was in my seventh heaven! She took me to a small cafe and treated me to tea and cakes. I kept telling everyone in the cafe what a wonderful sister she was until she told me to 'Hush!'

She asked me about Suffolk, and the Stophers. I told her how very good they had been to me. Then we went down to the harbour and sat on the quayside. She told me all about our Mother and Father and our lives in Belfast: how ill I was when we entered the Homes, how she had cried and cried at the hospital because everyone thought I would die.

'Never forget what you owe the Homes. Never, never. You owe them your life,' she said. 'I'll never forget because of them I still have you.'

'Do you remember the sugar lump episode?' I asked.

'I certainly do!' she replied. 'But remember for every bad matron like that one there are a lot more good ones.'

I told her about the lady who had taken away the pain on the third night of my punishment.

'So that's what you were on about. You kept on and on about it, asking where the lady had gone, but I never knew which lady you were talking about.'

She asked me if I was happy at the Naval School, and I assured her that I was. It was too nice a day to mention Yearly.

I told her how much I enjoyed seamanship, signals and all the sport. She told me that she had no idea where the army would be sending her. She gave me an army address to write to so that my letters could be forwarded to her.

The time flew and we had to return on board. Matron kindly let us use her room for a few moments before I escorted my sister to the entrance of the School.

How happy and proud I was to see the two Quartermasters present arms, and the Officer of the Day salute her as she marched out. I admired her smart salute in return.

I was not to see my sister again until years later in Alexandria.

Not long after my sister's visit I had another of those mystery experiences of my life.

It was my week as dormitory boy, and on Saturday evenings one of my duties was to lay out the number one uniform on each boy's bed. When I picked up one of the uniforms I could see the anchor on its sleeve, so I placed it on the bed of Leading Hand Brown. I came to the last uniform of the pile and saw it had an anchor on its sleeve, so carried it to L.H. Brown's bed, thinking he had two number one uniforms, but on reaching his bed I found that the uniform I had just put there did not have an anchor on its sleeve any longer: instead there was my number—109. It didn't make sense. I could have sworn I'd seen an anchor on the sleeve when I'd picked it up a few minutes before.

Two Sundays later, on Parade, I was called out of the ranks and made Auxilliary Leading Hand. It was quite unexpected.

Then one day we had an air raid around 1200 hours. The Germans bombed the harbour and the 'All Clear' didn't sound until 1330 hours, which meant we had a cold dinner.

It was Leading Hand Brown's last night. After lights out we all crowded round his bed to wish him good luck and safe voyages at sea. In the morning, spot on 0900 hours, he would march out, the

Quartermasters presenting arms, the Officer of the Day saluting.

How we all envied him and wished it was us going to sea! I was at least thirty months behind L.H. Brown, and even with the war and many seamen dying and replacements for them needed, I couldn't see myself getting away to sea in the next two years.

How fortunate it is that we can't know the future.

Leading Hand Brown had a wonderful rapport with all the boys in Howard House; he had never been known to hit a boy, or put anyone on defaulters unfairly.

At midnight the bugler played the alarm for a practice air raid.

I gave out the blankets as the boys rushed to the shelter and, getting to the last one, I reported to Leading Hand Brown who was waiting at the bottom of the landing to inform him that my dormitory was empty. We both rushed to the shelter. On the way I said, 'Just our luck! We had a real raid today and they wake us for a practice! You'd think they would let us sleep.' And then I thought no more about it.

Unbeknown to me, L.H. Brown told P.O. Gover, 'Poor old Titch is upset about losing his beauty sleep. He thinks the real alarm we had today was enough without this at midnight!'

P.O. Gover passed my remarks on to the Officer on Watch. He entered them in the log book.

It was what Lieutenant Commander Yearly had been waiting for.

At 0930 hours the next morning he entered our classroom. Everyone stood up and the teacher called everyone to attention.

Yearly told the teacher he was taking over and the teacher went and sat at the back of the class. Telling us to stand at ease, Yearly started by asking if we all knew what a Fifth Columnist was.

We assured him we did.

Did we know what a Quisling was?

Again we assured him we did.

'What should be done with Quislings and traitors?' asked Yearly.

'Hang them! Shoot them!' we all shouted.

'What would you say if I told you that they had infiltrated into the Navy? Even into this School? That we have one in our midst? Someone going around criticising officers' decisions and doing his best to undermine his officers' orders and authority?'

There was a gasp in the class. It was as if every boy knew

someone was in trouble. In the silence you could have heard a pin drop.

Yearly walked along the rows of desks until he reached me; then, with a look of pure hate, he hit me. As I started to fall he hit me again and I actually left the deck. He shouted and screamed vile words at me.

The teacher rushed forward, standing between Yearly and me, saying, 'Sir! Sir! Please, sir!'

Yearly was shaking all over, white with rage.

Then he said, 'Make sure O'Dell is on the Parade Ground in fifteen minutes!' and left the classroom.

The teacher sent the P.O. for a wet cloth to wipe my face and clean me up.

'My God O'Dell! What have you been doing?' the teacher asked.

Between sobs of rage and bewilderment I answered, 'I don't know, Sir.' So the teacher sent the P.O. to see if he could find out.

On his return the P.O. told the teacher what was written in the daily order book.

'Good grief! Are you telling me this is all because a young boy made a remark about wanting to sleep?'

'Yes Sir,' replied the P.O.

The teacher accompanied me to the Parade Ground, where he was promptly sent back to the classroom.

Yearly had a placard which read:

'I AM A NAZI' and got a P.O. to hang this on me. I was ordered to march up and down the Parade Ground, quick march, slow march, then run, then march, until the boys came out for the mid-morning break. Then I was marched to the mast and made to stand to attention until the end of the break when I was taken back to the Parade Ground and ordered to continue marching. I thought my lungs would burst. Eventually, my legs gave way and I was then marched up to Howard House.

Matron, shocked at my appearance, ordered a hot bath and put me to bed. Then she went down to see the Chief Officer: what transpired between Matron, Chief Officer and Yearly I never knew.

The boys in the dormitory were sympathetic, but frightened.

I was full of rage, humiliation and shame.

I spoke to no-one, not even Matron. I, who loved my Navy, my country, had been subjected to such degradation! I felt defiled. In me was a deep hatred for the man who had heaped this on me. I wanted to kill him.

The following Sunday, I was told that I should be taking Leading Hand Brown's place. I refused and asked to leave the Naval School. The Chief Officer, Matron and P.T. Officer all tried to get me to change my mind, but as far as I was concerned I had to get out. My whole being was full of hate. I could hardly keep my food down: my stomach kept churning; I vomited constantly. Sleep was hard to come by—as soon as I put my head down, waves of hatred swept over me. I snarled at everyone. I left the band and didn't bother with seamanship, gym work or sport. I was put on defaulters time after time, but none of the punishments bothered me. I just did everything as if in a dream: hatred kept me from any other emotion.

Two months later, when the next batch of boys left the Naval School on account of bad school marks and eyesight, I went with them.

I bade no-one but the Matron good-bye. She assured me she would pray for me, and for the hate to leave my heart. I told her not to bother: if there had been anyone up there He would not have made me suffer as I had. She was shocked, but I just walked away from her.

Chapter Ten

ON THE *S.S. LLANDUDNO*

'So now, Master, you know the reason why I left Naval School.'

The Master answered, 'Now O'Dell, you mustn't talk like that. You're off to sea. Try to put all that behind you.'

O'Dell leaned forward and said, 'Master, one day I'm going back for Yearly, and when I do it won't be any surprise to me if I kill him. I hate him far more that I hate any German.'

The Master looked into his eyes and knew he meant every word. Then he got up and said, 'Well, O'Dell, I'm off to bed. See you in the morning.'

O'Dell stayed in the kitchen for a while, then went back to the dormitory. Sleep wouldn't come. His thoughts were a mixture of Yearly and going to sea. Yet somehow he felt better for telling the Master, as if sharing his hate made it an easier burden to carry.

Years later, in the 1946/47 period, when he was on board a ship with the Reverend Snowdon Smith, one of the bosses of the Homes, O'Dell told him the story of Yearly and the Naval School. The Reverend said, 'Thomas, when we started to receive letters near or at the end of the war, complaining of treatment some of the old boys and girls had received, we honestly thought the first lot of letters had been from some unfortunates who were shell-shocked. I see we were mistaken.'

Sleep came fitfully to O'Dell that night and at 0700 hours he was awake and under the shower, then down to breakfast with the House Master, Staff and four other boys waiting to ship out.

Two of the boys had actually seen the *S.S. Llandudno* before him, but they hadn't wanted to ship out on such a dirty old tramp. There was a lot of good natured banter.

'You will starve to death on that old wreck!'

'You only picked that ship O'Dell because you know the German U-boats won't waste an expensive torpedo on her!'

After breakfast the House Master took him into his office.

'Well O'Dell,' said the Master. 'I have to confess your story has left me deeply unhappy. I have, of course, heard about Yearly from other boys who have passed through, but yours is by far the worst, and I'm deeply sorry you're going out into the world with such hatred in your heart. I want you to think of your future, so please try and eradicate the hate from your heart. Hate is so self-destructive. Yearly's not worth it. The other thing that disturbs me is your fear of water and what would happen if your ship is sunk.'

'Never fear, Master,' O'Dell answered. 'If we're sunk I promise to move so fast I will be first in the lifeboat or raft!'

The Master gave him five shillings, and the mandatory bible, which everyone leaving the Homes received, which O'Dell was to keep for the rest of his life.

He said good-bye to everyone, and although it was only 0900 hours he slung the kit bag over his shoulder, clutched the small case in his right hand and marched down Caernarvon Road to the shipping office: he was there well before 1100 hours.

Prompt on 1100 hours he signed on the *S.S. Llandudno* as Mess Boy, for the magnificent sum of two pounds five shillings per month, all found. He had no discharge book, no Merchant Navy I.D. card, no medical examination; all he had, clutched in his hand, was a receipt for the two shillings joining fee from the Seamen's Union. He received his I.D. card two days later.

When it is considered how much paraphernalia there is to go through today to sign on it may be realised how bureaucracy has created jobs for the boys.

After signing on, O'Dell rushed down to the ship, only to find it deserted. Everyone had either gone to the dock canteen or the dock-side pub for lunch. The ship would not start feeding the crew officially until the next day.

When the officers returned, O'Dell reported to the Chief Engineer, who sent him to the dock-side canteen for a meal with a chitty to charge it to the *S.S. Llandudo*. He felt so proud handing the chitty to the lady in charge, telling her he was a new member of the crew, but it did not seem to have any effect on the lady: she just took the cigarette out of her mouth and shouted to someone, 'Bring another rabbit stew for a late comer!' He felt deflated and somehow let down.

On his return to the ship the Chief took him round to a wide alleyway on the starboard side, where the deck apprentices were housed: the Third Radio Operator, Catering Staff and toilets.

This alleyway was identical to the one on the portside in so far as the accommodation was also right up to the ship's side, with each end open to the elements at sea.

After showing him his cabin the Chief left him, and he soon discovered he had to share the cabin with two other boys, both of whom had signed on as Officers' Boys.

The cabin was twelve by nine feet. There were three bunks, one centre light with no shade, two oil lamps fixed to the bulkhead pivots so that they swung in the ship's motion at sea. There was one three foot settee, one stove (or bogie), one coal scuttle and one compactum with tin underneath. The lino was very worn and faded; it appeared to have had a pattern on it at one time; this covered the deck and he loved every inch of it. This was to be his new home. He felt so lucky, so grateful: he was truly happy and contented.

Opposite the exit from the cabin was the engine-room casing; there was a door in this casing which gave access over the top of the engine-room to a door that opened opposite the Engineer's Saloon. How he was going to bless that short cut to the Engineers' accommodation during the bad weather in the voyage ahead!

Since he was the first to arrive, he picked the bottom bunk and the best tin locker for his clothes.

The Chief had told him that although he did not officially start until the next day, if he wished he could draw his bedding issue and get settled in by going to see the Chief Steward.

The Chief Steward issued him with a donkey's breakfast (that is, a straw mattress) which had definitely seen better days, two thin grey blankets, and two thin pillows, both badly stained with sweat marks from previous owners. He was also given a large bar of soda soap, an aluminium bucket and a tin of condensed milk, which the Chief Steward said had to last him three weeks, together with two small wood plugs which, it was explained, he was to use once he had punched two holes in the milk tin—to keep the cockroaches out.

He returned to the cabin and made up his bunk. then returned to the Chief Steward and collected the Engineers' store issues, and cleaning gear.

He learnt from the chief engineer that the Engineers had a break at 1500 hours, so just before they were due, O'Dell made tea and toast. Then, prompt at 1500 hours, he went to find the engineers who had gone on deck for a breather after the hard graft and heat of the engine room. Forgetting the chief's instructions on reaching the engineers, he slammed his foot down and stood stiffly at attention, assured the Second Engineer Officer that 'Your tea and toast is ready Sir.' The dockers and the deck crew fell about laughing.

However with a smile he was trying hard to suppress, the Second Engineer Officer thanked him and went towards the Engineer's Saloon, followed by O'Dell accompanied by a barrage of calls behind him from the deck crew; 'Attention! Your tea Sir! Three bags full Sir!' with a lot of banging of feet. The Second turned and said, 'Don't mind them, Bach.'

O'Dell grinned. 'Oh I don't, Second! I asked for it, but a little flak like that will teach me to remember I'm in the Merchant Navy.'

'That's the ticket!' said the Second.

When the Engineers had gone back down to the engine room, the Chief sat him down in the saloon and explained once again that no one in the Merchant Navy is called 'Sir', or saluted; not even the Captain.

'So, Bach, no more Sirs or saluting—understand?'

O'Dell did understand, but it was hard to break the habit of years.

'I realise that,' said the Chief, 'but for your sake you must break it or the crew will be taking the mickey for a long time to come.'

That night, when everyone had gone ashore or to their quarters, O'Dell started on the Engineer's pantry. He had given the job a lot of thought and decided if Mess Boy was the only job he could get, then he would try to be the best Mess Boy the *S.S. Llandudno* had ever had.

He decided to put all longing to be on deck aside until the end of the voyage.

The pantry was filthy. He had to scrub and scrub down the bulkheads with soda soap and Vim: he heated water by standing the bucket on top of the stove in the saloon.

He had just finished polishing the mahogany cupboards and started on the sink, when the Chief arrived back with the Captain and an Army officer. He managed not to spring to attention with great effort.

'What are you doing boyo?' asked the Chief. 'Don't you remember what I told you? There's no need for you to start until tomorrow.'

'Yes, Chief, but I thought as I was not going ashore I'd get started tonight. Is that all right?'

'All right by me, boyo,' replied the Chief. 'But I think you should finish now. Before you go—who do you think this is?' He pointed to the Army officer.

O'Dell looked at the officer, who stood there, smiling.

'Oh that's easy Chief. That's the one and only Jackie Petersen, the greatest boxer, pound for pound in weight for over seventy years!' Petersen smiled. He shook O'Dell's hand and said, 'You'd better not let Tommy Farr hear you say that!'

As O'Dell turned to leave the Captain asked him, 'Are you from one of the naval schools run by Homes?'

'Yes, Captain.'

'I thought so. We had one on board here about three years ago. Why aren't you on deck? That's what you train for, isn't it?'

'Yes, Captain, but I couldn't get a deck job, even after tramping the docks for four days.'

'By the way,' said the Chief as O'Dell reached the door, 'you'll be called by Abdul every morning at 0600 hours, in port or at sea, for the rest of this voyage.'

O'Dell left them then and went to his cabin. Lighting the two oil lamps, he wrote a letter to the Homes, thanking them for all they had done for him in the past fourteen years and for saving his life when he left Belfast. He told them he had a job on the S.S. Llandudno as Mess Boy; he liked the ship; he was very happy: and he promised to let them know how he got on.

Next morning prompt at 0600 hours, he was awakened by Abdul.

Abdul turned out to be the Number One Donkeyman. After introducing himself to O'Dell, he explained what was to be done: first to make and serve tea to all the Engineers except the Chief. No-one but Abdul served the Chief with his tea. In port all Engineers were to be called by 0700 hours.

After he had washed, O'Dell arrived at the engineers' pantry to find Abdul had already boiled the water on the stove for him, so he made the tea and served it to the Engineers in their bunks. He then laid up the table for their breakfast, which in port was always served at 0800 hours.

Somehow that first hour really brought home to O'Dell the fact that he was in the catering, and truly signified the end of his dream of working on deck. He was, for this voyage at least, what the Navy called a piss pot jerker. He recalled the contempt the lads in the Naval School had for anyone in catering, and was glad they could not see him now. He had yet to learn that the job does not make the man.

After breakfast the Chief explained all his duties. In port breakfast was at 0800 hours, dinner at 1230 hours, tea at 1700 hours. As there was no running water, Abdul, or one of his men, would bring hot water for washing up at each meal time from the engine room. Under no circumstance was he ever to enter the Chief s quarters: only Abdul would keep it clean.

'You understand Bach? Never, never enter my quarters.' He told the Chief he understood.

That day was to turn out an exciting one: he met his two cabin mates for the first time. They were both a couple of years older than him. One was called Jack McSally and he had already done a voyage on the ship to Canada and back; the other lad was, like O'Dell himself, a first tripper called Ron Travers. Since both these boys lived in Cardiff they would not be living on board until the ship sailed.

Jack wanted to take over the bunk O'Dell had selected, but Ron, who was twice the size of Jack, thought that as O'Dell had to sleep on board and had been first to join, it was only fair he should keep the lower bunk. They made an agreement to keep the cabin clean by a weekly rota: decisions were to be taken by vote which, of course, would always work out two to one, for or against.

After dinner the Chief said he had arranged for one of the deck apprentices to take O'Dell shopping to Moses, the ship's clothing supplier, to select a few items he would need for sea and for work.

'We can't have you in that uniform,' explained the Chief. The Chief asked if he had any money.

'Yes Sir' said O'Dell.

97

The deck apprentice turned out to be the boy he had passed on deck the first time he had come on board. His name was Ian Sims and he was eighteen years old. On the way to Moses, Ian asked O'Dell why he was in uniform and he explained about the Naval School.

'So you know Morse, seamanship and semaphore?' said Ian.

'Oh yes. I had cross flags at the Naval School.' Then he asked Ian about the *S.S. Llandudno* and her officers.

'Tell you what,' said Ian, 'after we've finished at Moses, we'll go and have a cup of tea and a good yarn.'

Going to Moses' shop was another milestone in O'Dell's life. It was the first time he had gone into a shop to buy something with his own money.

Moses was the cheapest dockside shop in Cardiff, and under Ian's kind guidance he bought two pairs of canvas trousers, two thick cloth shirts, one set of khaki shirt and shorts, two pairs of strong boots, one pair of black shoes, one pair of Wellingtons, one pair of thick sea socks. He also bought two tablets of soap, and Moses threw in one toothbrush and toothpaste free. The whole account came to eleven shillings.

Once the two boys had settled into the cafe with their tea and buns, Ian proceeded to give him the complete run down of the ship and its officers. He told O'Dell that the *S.S. Llandudno* had been built in 1912, was 3,620 nett tonnage and was of the type usually called a Three Island Ship, except that she had a small bunker hatch between the Bridge accommodation and the Midship accommodation.

The Bridge accommodation housed the Captain, three Mates, two Radio Operators and the Chief Steward.

The Midship accommodation housed the Engineer's port side, then the boys starboard side, all accommodation being wall side on; that is to the ship's side.

The Amidship accommodation had inboard alleyways open at both ends, and therefore open to the elements at sea. In extremely bad weather the ends were sealed off by fitting storm boards of three inch thick mahogany into steel channels installed at each end.

The ship had what is called a raised forecastle head, and Number One hatch was in what is called a well deck. Numbers Two and Three hatches were on the same level as the deck houses and Midship accommodation, while Number Four hatch was in the aft well deck.

The Galley ran athwart ship at the end of the engine room casing. Outside the Galley was a pump where drinking water could be drawn.

Steering was from the Bridge or Docking Bridge by means of chains; these massive chains ran from the bridge down the port side, around the counter stern, then up starboard side, back to the Bridge. They could be heard every night over the heads of the crew as the chains rattled, groaned and scraped with every movement of the ship as it was steered at sea.

The deck and engine crew lived right aft under the Poop and Docking Bridge, which was raised above the Counter Stern. The deck and engine crew accommodation was separated only by a canvas curtain, and they could only reach their quarters by the Well Deck.

There was a gun platform raised right aft over the Poop for the new 4.5 gun, which had just been received. The ship also had a Lewis gun on each wing of the Bridge.

The D.E.M.S. gunners who manned the guns were housed in newly-built accommodation in Number Three hatch between decks.

Ian then described the personnel of the *Llandudno*.

The Captain was thirty nine years old. He joined the ship as a deck apprentice and worked his way up to Master, the only voyage he had missed was while sitting his tickets. His pet hates were Radio Operators.

The First Mate was fifty seven, an ex-harbour Master, ex-ship's Master, and now First Mate, brought down by the booze.

The Second Mate was sixty one, had been ashore since 1928, working in a biscuit factory, then called back to sea by the war.

Third Mate was the Senior Deck Apprentice from the previous voyage. He had no certificates yet and he was still serving his time.

There were three Radio Operators and another deck apprentice.

The Chief Engineer was fifty years old and had been on board the ship since 1917. He was Chief when the Captain first joined the ship as an apprentice. The Chief always brought his parrot, Popeye, with him to sea. Ian assured O'Dell that was a pleasure yet to come to meet this bird!

The Second Engineer had also been called back to sea. He was sixty, and had been working ashore at Spillers since 1930.

The Third Engineer was twenty four, with no certificate.

The Fourth Engineer was a first tripper, who had just finished serving his time in a garage in Canton, Cardiff. He was twenty one.

All firemen, trimmers and the two donkeymen were Arabs. The deck crew, including Carpenter, Bosun and Lamp Trimmer, were all Welsh.

'In fact, Titch,' said Ian, 'apart from the Radio Operators, I think you're the only non-Welshman on board.'

After this long chat, Ian said, 'I'm off home now, Titch.'

'Could you spare just a few more minutes? Will you tell me what is a Trimmer? And what duties do Lamp Trimmers have?'

'A Trimmer is the man who keeps the fireman supplied with coal from the side bunkers to stoke-hold fires with his wheelbarrow. A Lamp Trimmer trims the ships side lights, bridge lights, and keeps all oil lamps in first class condition. He looks after all deck stores paints, ships ropes and chipping hammers and so on.'

'Don't we have electric side-lights nowadays?'

Ian laughed. 'Not on old ships like the S.S. Llandudno,' he replied.

O'Dell arrived back at the ship in time to see the D.E.M.S. gunners arriving, and remembered just in time not to salute the Petty Officer in charge. He noticed the P.O. and the D.E.M.S. gunners giving him the once-over as he climbed the gangway.

That night he started on cleaning the engineers' saloon while they were ashore. It was a hard job. The dirt and coal dust was ground in. However after using some vinegar, then polishing with Ronuk he managed to get the beautiful wood surround fairly clean, but realised it would take a few more hours of hard rubbing to get it up to standard.

Next morning he was up and raring to go even before Abdul called him.

It was a day of another milestone. He left his bed unmade and all crumpled up. Only someone who has had to make his bed to precise specifications, exactly six inches from the ground all round, four inches exactly in the corner folds, nine inches exactly in the counterpane fold down, measured by a Matron, can know the sheer and utter joy and pleasure to leave a bed unmade.

Oh, the sheer exquisite feeling of freedom that he could never put into words!

At breakfast the Chief and the others congratulated him on the new-look saloon, and after the meal the Chief told him not to bother with the Engineers' cabins, except to make up their bunks and empty the compactums, until the ship left port.

That morning he met the Cook and Galley Boy: both were black. The Cook had been born in the West Indies, but lived in Cardiff and was forty one years old. The Galley Boy, although very black, was born in Cardiff. It seemed strange to hear him speak with such a lovely Welsh lilt. O'Dell had met only two other blacks before: one at the B.G.C. and one at Suffolk. They intrigued him.

Next day everyone was ordered to attend boat drill on the boat deck and to draw their lifejackets and light. O'Dell arrived in his new working gear and the deck crew started to tease him in a good natured way, asking, 'Who is this man out of uniform?' Shouting, 'Attention! Here comes the Navy!' and 'Let's see you bang your foot down Titch!' O'Dell joined in the laughter; it was meant kindly and helped to break the ice.

The Petty Officer of the D.E.M.S. came over to him and asked him about the uniform. O'Dell explained about the Naval School and training.

'Oh I know about them,' exclaimed the P.O. 'I've sailed with many a lad from there. Mind you, I've been retired more than seven years, and now they've called me back to colours. They are so short of manpower. But I thought they trained boys like you for deck?'

'They do, P.O., but I couldn't get a deck job. Anyway, I'm very happy with my job here, and the Chief and the other engineers have made me very welcome.'

'What a waste!' grunted the P.O. 'A piss pot jerker—after all that training!'

The Second Mate issued the life jackets with the help of Ian. They were the old-fashioned sort and the Second showed everyone how to hold the front of the jacket tight down if they had to jump into the sea. He told all hands that if they did not do this the two large lumps in front would snap their heads back and break their necks. Then he made everyone clip on their red lights to the lifejackets and test them to see that they did light up.

After this, all hands had to help swing the boats out, then back in on the davits. This was all manual labour: no machine to help with lifeboats on board the *S.S. Llandudno*.

Before leaving the boat deck the Chief Steward explained that the catering staff were the ship's first aiders and stretcher bearers, if there were accidents on board at any time the catering staff were to report to him for first aid duties, and especially if action station sounded. This was a great surprise to him, but McSally assured both him and Travers it was the same on every Merchant Navy ship.

That afternoon in his off duty break O'Dell went ashore and bought a First Aid book from Moses' store. He felt that if he had to be in the First Aid section he had better know something about it.

When he arrived back on board he was introduced to the famous parrot, Popeye, which the Chief had brought back on board; he had put up wires criss-crossing the Engineers' saloon, even extending them into the Chief's own quarters.

As O'Dell stepped over the storm step, he heard a voice say, 'Silly old Popeye!'—and there was the parrot, rushing along the wire towards him. As it swung down and tried to pull his hair, he quickly ducked and the parrot turned and did its business on him! The engineers roared with laughter, for it appeared this was one of Popeye's tricks: if he missed your hair in flight he got you with his mess!

The parrot had been with the Chief for fifteen years, but despite this it certainly was not house trained, but did its business everywhere and anywhere: on settee, chairs, deck and table, whether anyone was eating or not. It seemed to particularly like doing a mess in the soup if the lid was left off, or in the vegetable dishes, so that it became a contest of how fast you could serve, remembering to keep the lids handy at all times.

It was a brave engineer who complained about Popeye, as he swung up and down the wires. The Chief could not bear any criticism of the parrot and would tolerate no remarks against what the Third Engineer Officer was to call 'That Bloody Bird!'

In the really hot weather to come, Popeye was to cause some bitter exchanges in the engineers' saloon, especially one particular morning off Aden, when Popeye messed right on the Third Engineer Officer's paw paw at breakfast. The Third became so enraged that before the

Chief could stop him he got a cleaver from the galley and threw it at Popeye, but missed the bird. Then he picked up the cleaver and, holding the Chief at bay, slashed down all the wires. The Chief and Abdul spent all morning putting them up again, and for about a week the Third ate his meals standing up, as O'Dell had to do in the pantry.

Just as O'Dell thought his day was finished, the Chief Steward came for him to help stow the meats and fish which were just coming on board, plus barrels of salt pork and beef, and the dry stores (grocery items). There was no fridge on board so the sides of beef, mutton, pork, sausage, liver and kidney were lowered into a large tank, which could only be entered through the same trap door that the meats went through. After what seemed to O'Dell to be a lot of meat, the fish was then lowered in, followed by large blocks of ice. When the tank was full to the top the lid was lowered down and sealed ready for the voyage. A tap at the bottom of the tank, which opened near number four hatch, was opened each day to let the melted ice run away.

The salt meat, in barrels, and salt fish were stored in a room under the Bridge, together with the flour, salt bags and other dry stores. The storeroom was thick with cockroaches and rats.

On the boat deck the forty bags of potatoes were stowed in the potato locker, and thirty bags of mixed carrot and turnips in the vegetable locker, then the lockers were padlocked to stop the crew getting at them.

It was 2100 hours by the time they finished, and the Chief Steward reminded them there would be no overtime as the work came under preparing for sea, but he did give them a tin of sweets each.

Next day they sailed out of Cardiff docks to the bay off Milford Haven. O'Dell stood on deck watching everything, feeling so proud that he was off to sea. He wanted to shout to the dockers and lock keepers that *S.S. Llandudno* was sailing, but in reality hardly a soul even bothered to look up as they proceeded out.

Next morning he woke to find they had company. A few ships had joined them in the night. It was the start of a convoy.

A navy trawler and destroyer began lamping at day-break, informing the ships to line up for target practice, two tugs pulling a large target behind them.

It was nearly midday by the time it was the *Llandudno's* turn.

The P.O. and six D.E.M.S. ratings were manning the newly installed 4.5 gun aft, while the Lewis guns on the wings of the Bridge were manned by two D.E.M.S. ratings to each Lewis.

Everyone that could be there was on deck to watch the christening of the 4.5 gun.

As the target was towed past on the starboard side, the P.O. shouted the orders and one of the ratings-pulled the lanyard. There was one hell of a loud bang, and an awful scream as a D.E.M.S. rating flew through the air. The poor old *Llandudno* gave a lurch sideways, then keeled over on her port side and everyone not holding on was thrown across the deck. For a terrible moment O'Dell thought she was going to turn completely over.

When the ship straightened up the alarm bells were ringing. O'Dell looked aft and saw the P.O. and others playing out the fire hose. The gun had broken at its casing; the trunk split wide open exposing a thick large spring that had snapped; the breech block was now embedded into the new gun platform, while the barrel of the 4.5 was looking up into the sky, quite broken and forlorn. One D.E.M.S. gunner lay on number four hatch, another was being lowered off the gun platform by the Bosun and some of his men leaped forward to help the D.E.M.S. and put out the fire. A destroyer raced alongside, lamping a request to know what the hell had gone wrong and to tell the Captain to move the ship out of line until the damage had been assessed.

From the Galley came shouts of rage from the cook. All his pots and pans had left the stove and landed on deck. The cook was not amused and the midday meal was ruined. The Chief Steward rushed past with the stretcher. 'Come on Titch!' shouted McSally as he ran past.

O'Dell ran to join them. At number four hatch the D.E.M.S. rating was in great pain. He had broken his leg in three places and smashed his right shoulder blade, as it turned out. They strapped him in the stretcher and carried him Amidship. The other D.E.M.S. rating had broken both his wrists.

The Captain was in a foul mood, and could be heard shouting at the Radio Operators to signal faster to the Navy escorts.

When the midday meal was served it was corned beef, tinned beans and potatoes. No one ate the potatoes, as all hands were convinced the Cook and Galley Boy had scraped them up from the galley deck which was covered in ash and cockroaches. Extra bread was also served.

After the meal, while O'Dell was standing on deck at number three hatch, a destroyer approached and started lamping. Without thinking he said to the P.O., 'They want the ship to proceed towards Milford Haven. A tug and tender is on its way out to meet us and on the tug is a Navy Officer coming to get a full statement from you. Also you are to see the injured D.E.M.S. ratings on to the tender, with four other D.E.M.S. ratings and all their gear. With the 4.5 gun out of action, only yourself and four ratings are to proceed on the voyage.'

There was silence all round him, then the P. O. said, 'Are you telling me you can read what they are lamping?'

'Oh yes P.O.,' O'Dell replied. 'I told you I had cross flags for signals at the Naval School.'

Then he heard the Chief Engineer's voice. 'What are they signalling now Bach?'

O'Dell looked at the destroyer which was lamping fast.

'They've just said that it should not delay us joining the convoy.' The Chief Engineer moved off.

The P. O. said, 'Good grief! If you can read like that you're wasted as a piss pot jerker.'

'I told you P.O. I couldn't get a deck job.'

'It's still a bloody waste of training Titch!' said the P.O.

They reached the tug and accompanying tender and transferred the D.E.M.S. ratings. The old *S.S. Llandudno* then rejoined the other ships, and moved out to sea to join the rest of the convoy. All lifeboats were swung out and lashed to the booms ready for a quick release if the ship should be torpedoed.

Next morning, after a night in which the ship pitched, rolled and shook and the steering chain rattled, scraped and groaned over their heads, O'Dell felt ill. In fact he was very seasick.

When Abdul called him at 0600 hours he felt like death. Abdul told him he must turn to and work.

'Better you work than lie down,' Abdul assured him. How he got through the day he never knew. The Chief also forbade him to lie down. 'Work and eat plenty of dry biscuits' was the Chief's advice.

O'Dell was so ill he forgot to plug the two holes in the top of his condensed milk tin, with the result that the cockroaches poured in, and when he went to put milk in his tea, they flowed out.

This sight made him feel even worse, but the Senior Officer's boy, McSally, managed to sneak him another tin from the storeroom, with a strong warning to keep the holes plugged up. 'You won't get another tin for three weeks,' he was told.

O'Dell was to remain seasick all the way up the Irish coast.

By now they had joined up with the main convoy, and in their allotted position in the fourth column, but O'Dell felt so ill he could not have cared less. He just wanted to die.

It wore off eventually. But at the time it was a terrible feeling. One of the first shocks he received on sailing was the toilet which was not used in port. It came as a great surprise when, not long after sailing, McSally stripped off, and advised O'Dell and Travers to do the same, whenever they wanted the toilet until the ship hit calm weather. While O'Dell was ill he forgot McSally's warning and, after managing to heave the solid steel door open (it was held closed by the strongest spring he had ever encountered), he scrambled inside to find two large concrete steps, each two feet high, on top of which was the throne. He reached the throne, dropped his trousers, and there was a mighty roar as the sea came charging up, nearly washing him off the throne. The toilet on the *S. S. Llandudno* ran straight out to sea, hence there was no need for a flushing device. The only trouble, of course, was that in rough weather everything got washed up and down!

McSally and Travers held their sides with laughter as he staggered back in, soaked to the skin. Then they threw him out and would not let him back in again until he stood on deck, holding tight to the storm rope and let the waves wash him clean from his own toilet. Using the toilet in bad weather was another version of getting your own back, that is doing it against the wind.

After that first encounter, he stripped off in rough weather like everyone else. Of course, for normal relief, everyone just did it over the ship's side, or a corner of the deck if the wind was too frisky.

Though the weather remained wet, grey and choppy, once he was over the seasickness he found he enjoyed the daily routine. The worst part of the job, as far as he was concerned, was having to carry tea down to the Second Engineer Officer every morning, climbing down the ladders, one hand holding the rail and in the other a mug of tea. As the ship rolled and pitched he felt this was quite an achievement, especially as it was all of seventy feet to the engine room platform.

Four days out from Cardiff they lost their first ship. O'Dell was on deck looking at the convoy rolling and labouring along, when he heard the thud, crump. An A.B. going past him shouted, 'That was a torpedo, Titch. Better get your lifejacket on!'

He saw a cloud of smoke, and the escort ships racing around, then the crump, crump, of depth charges. He realised with a tingle of fear and excitement that there was a U-boat around; that danger was lurking just below the waves.

The alarm bells sounded. A destroyer tore past, flying the black pennant signalling that there were U-boats about. All hands went to their action stations, while O'Dell joined the rest of the catering staff outside the Chief Steward's quarters inside the accommodation. He could not make up his mind how he felt. His stomach was churning, yet there was a definite tingle of adventure.

He was aware without any doubt that he was in the wrong position. He longed to be on deck, or better still on the bridge signalling, certainly not cowering inside an alleyway waiting for others to get hurt.

When the 'All Clear' sounded he felt depressed, as if he had been hiding while those on deck and down in the engine room had faced the danger.

He tried to put his feelings into words to McSally and the Galley Boy, but they looked at him as if he was a mental case. Travers later told him he knew what O'Dell meant, but added, 'Better to be alive than a dead hero, O'Dell.'

Around this time they came to realise they could not sleep in the hard cork lifejackets, so they used them as pillows, making them handy to put on fast.

The food on board was turning out to be no better nor worse than O'Dell was used to, except for the bread, and the evening meal. There was still only one egg every fourth Sunday. The average week consisted of cereal, salt bacon or fried Spam or salt fish and rice for breakfast; some kind of meat, with vegetable and potatoes for dinner;

and for the evening meal fish dish, or Boston Baked Beans, or blind scouse (or hot pot made from meat leftovers chopped up).

Dessert was only issued twice a week, on Sundays and Thursdays. It was always the same dessert, served on every British ship all over the world: B.O.T. (Board of Trade) duff: steamed fruit pudding and custard. The Board of Trade required all crews to be served two sweets a week and the shipping companies served the easiest and cheapest. Hence the expression 'B.O.T. duff'!

Sometimes the cook gave everyone a surprise and served up stewed dried apple rings or dried, stewed prunes for breakfast, or the evening meal.

After about eleven days out in the Atlantic, the convoy split up, half to carry on across the Atlantic to Halifax, Canada. The other half, including the *Llandudno* was to change course for South Africa.

After a lot of lamping and chivvying from the escorts, the new convoy for South Africa settled into four new columns; the old *Llandudno* now the last ship in column three.

That night they had a visit from the U-boats. The ships in the van of column one and column two were both sunk, and just before dawn a tanker blew up. It was like a ball of fire and obvious that no one would survive that blast.

O'Dell felt sick, and not a little frightened. Certainly he did not want any breakfast.

The next night the weather turned really rough. The ship plunged, rolled, pitched, and shook all night. There was certainly no sleep to be had and for the first time waves were rushing past the cabin door, nearly lapping over the storm step. The steering chain excelled itself with its loud scrape, rattle and groan.

When dawn broke they were all up long before Abdul called them. McSally and Travers had to plunge out in their under-pants, holding tight to the storm rope with one hand, and holding their clothes above their heads with the other. McSally told O'Dell that if the weather got worse, he and Travers would spend the night in the storeroom on flour sacks.

O'Dell put his Wellingtons on and, as the ship raised its head and the waves cleared from the inboard alleyway for a few moments, he rushed across, opened the door in the engine room casing, and crossed over the top of the engine room to the door that opened to the Engineers' inboard alleyway. He then repeated this procedure and gained the Engineers Saloon. He had his lifejacket on, much to the amusement of the Chief and Abdul.

Abdul sent the tea down to the engine room by a trimmer, for which O'Dell was deeply grateful, for he was sure he could not have held on to the rails and tea at the same time in the rough weather.

Breakfast had just finished when there was a loud thump. It was so near he thought the ship had been hit, particularly as the *Llandudno* gave an awful lurch at the same time. But it was the ship opposite, in column two, that was hit.

O'Dell rushed to the porthole in time to see the ship break in half as huge waves swallowed her up.

As the alarm bells went off the Chief ordered him to stay in the saloon, and not to attempt to reach his action station. After stand down he heard the Chief say to the Third Engineer Officer, 'Now will you believe me when I tell you bad weather does not mean no U-boat attacks? Those bastards will attack in any weather.'

The weather got worse and the poor old Llandudno was taking a real beating. Just before light failed he looked through the porthole and saw high waves with thick white spume and spray folding over and crashing down.

The ship kept shuddering, the steering chain clanging. and scraping: things were getting worse by the hour.

Every time the governor cut out in the engine, the Chief would shout, 'Abdul! The governor!'

Abdul would shout back, 'I bloody know!'

When O'Dell went to collect the Boston Baked Beans he noticed that the large mahogany sleepers had been put across the inboard alleyway fore and aft. Yet still the waves dashed over. One such wave nearly washed him off his feet and against the sleepers as he carried the meals to the saloon. Only the Cook leaning out over the lower half of the galley door and grabbing him by his hair saved him, and the meal. Then he tried to thank the Cook, all Cook said was, 'Watch that bloody meal man! I've not gone to all that trouble for you to lose it!'

The Chief told him to sleep on the settee in the saloon for the night and not to attempt to reach his cabin in the bad weather.

What a night it was, the wind screeching and howling like a Banshee and the poor old ship thrown all over the ocean.

O'Dell gathered from what the Chief told the Engineer Officers at breakfast that the Captain was having a hard time trying to keep the ship head on, let alone moving. Also a ship ahead had turned over, as had one of the trawler escorts.

'If a trawler turns over it's got to be bad news,' said the Second Engineer.

Popeye the parrot did not seem to mind the weather as he swung up and down the wires. When not talking he kept cackling with laughter, over and over again as if he knew something no-one else did!

As the day passed the weather seemed to get even worse.

Nightfall saw O'Dell trying to sleep once again on the settee, but it was a fitful sleep. Somehow it seemed worse at night, and as the ship jarred and plunged he started to become afraid. Then, as if he had not got enough problems, Popeye twice decided to leave his wires and settle on him while it did its business.

Just as O'Dell was getting really frightened and was hugging himself in the corner of the settee, his lady came back. After all those years she came back, smiled, and faded away. But he somehow knew he was going to be all right. If anyone had asked him to describe her he could not have done it. Yet he saw the face and smile that he had seen all those years ago as a child in the dormitory. and he felt at peace with himself.

Daylight came and the weather was as bad as ever, but he felt different, and as he lifted the dead lights from the portholes, all he could see was mountainous waves and foaming white seas. The poor ship seemed to be down in a valley one minute, then climbing the sides of a mountainous sea the next. Just as she seemed to reach the top, huge waves seemed to grab her bows and pull her under again. Then the whole ship seemed to submerge, shuddering and shaking. It was truly frightening to see Nature in the raw.

How the Cook managed to produce any food at all was a miracle, yet at breakfast there was burrgoe and salt bacon, plus two loaves of bread.

The weather was so appalling that even the fiddle across the galley stove could not stop the pots and pans from flying through the air. It got worse, and the Chief was extremely worried about his engine and the poor firemen trying to shovel coal into the fires, as the ship threw them all over the place.

Then the old *Llandudno* shipped an extra large wave right over her bow. She seemed to wallow and shake, and the engine cut out. There was an eerie silence as the covering seas cut out the noise of the gale force winds. As the engine stopped for a moment it was like being buried alive in water and darkness. A weird feeling indeed.

Then somehow the dear old *Llandudno* managed to shake free and rise again as the engine cut in.

It was on the fourth morning, just after breakfast, that an enormous wave hit the *Llandudno* port side on. It seemed that this was the end. There came a terrible, horrid sound overhead from the boat deck, then the engine gave what sounded like a scream, and the ship shuddered to a stop, lying well over on her starboard side.

O'Dell rushed out of the pantry, just as the Chief shot out of his cabin shouting, 'She has stopped boyo! Get your life jacket on!'

The tearing, roaring sound continued. The ship lurched even more to starboard. Then all the lights went out.

The Chief in the meantime had got across to the engine room door and started down to the engine room. O'Dell heard afterwards how the Chief was met by the firemen trying to escape the nightmare below. The Chief cursed, kicked and knocked them back below.

After what seemed a long time, but was really only a minute or two, the ship just lay broached on. Then the wonderful old lady started to straighten up.

O'Dell tried to look out of the porthole, but there was nothing to see except churning, boiling, angry, white water. The thought crossed his mind that if the ship had turned over, no-one would ever had known how he had died.

Even Popeye was quiet and subdued, and from the galley came the Cook's usual curses and anger being vented.

Later that afternoon the wind seem to drop away as fast as it had come, although there were still some high waves.

Even to O'Dell's inexperienced eyes the worst seemed to be over. This was confirmed by the Chief when he came up from the engine room at 1700 hours to see if there was anything to eat.

111

Somehow the Cook had baked potatoes in the ovens, and then opened a few tins of minced beef and tins of tomatoes. Everyone from the Captain down got two baked potatoes, beef and tomatoes.

In that weather this was a miracle indeed.

At 1900 hours the Captain came down to see the Chief and from the pantry O'Dell heard the Captain telling the Chief that there was awful damage on deck. Part of the portside wing of the bridge had gone, and all the sandbags around the bridge which were protection against aircraft attacks.

The two lifeboats on the port side had gone, and there was a lot more damage on the boat deck which they could not assess until daylight.

The Captain continued, 'I thought the old woodbine funnel was going at one time. Thank goodness we had those new stays put around her last trip. As it is the top is slightly bent.'

The Chief then told the Captain about the damage in the engine room.

'I doubt whether you will get more than six knots out of her from here to South Africa,' he said. As it turned out, the Chief was an optimist. The grand old lady never did more than four knots all the way to Africa. O'Dell was told by the Chief that as the worst was over he could return to his cabin to sleep after he had emptied the slop bucket they had both used for toilet.

As he went to leave the Captain said, 'Well, boyo! What do you think of your first storm? Are you sorry you came to sea? Were you frightened?'

'Yes sir,' he replied. 'I was frightened, but no, I'm not sorry I came to sea. But do you get many storms like that?'

The Captain looked it the Chief, then said, 'No boyo. You don't get many storms like that. In fact that's the worst one I have ever experienced in all my years at sea, and I'm sure I speak for the Chief too.' The Chief nodded and the Captain continued.

'If you stay at sea until you're a hundred years old you won't see a storm like that again, boyo. The winds reached a hundred and twenty five miles an hour and the glass dropped twenty seven eighty.'

How wrong the Captain was. Twenty years later O'Dell was to sail through a hurricane with winds reaching a hundred and seventy two miles an hour and the glass at an all time low of 27.3. Thank goodness one cannot see into the future.

When he arrived back in the cabin, he found McSally and Travers there. They discussed the storm and shared experiences. They told him they had spent every night in the storeroom on the flour and rice sacks which they had shared with the cockroaches and rats.

McSally admitted he thought at one time the ship was going to turn over. The rats thought this too as they raced round and round in a panic, screeching and squealing something awful.

Travers admitted he had also been very frightened, and swore that he would never go to sea again once the voyage was over. He never did, and was to die in the Army in 1945.

The next day dawned to peaceful and warm sunshine. It was hard to imagine what they had just gone through until they went on deck.

The port side wing of the bridge and the boat deck had suffered most. What was left of the two port-side lifeboats hung in shreds from fore and aft davits. The booms of spars they were lashed to had also disappeared. The engine room and cabin air vents were crushed. Even the corners of the engine room skylights were buckled.

To see thick steel twisted and crushed like that brought home the strength and force of the winds and waves of the gale, and with it came a greater respect for the seas and Nature.

The potato locker had been torn from its deck lashings, but was still there, upside-down with the vegetables washed away. This was something everyone was going to regret later.

In the afternoon a delegation from deck and engine room staff plus Travers met the Captain, and respectfully asked him to change course and head for the nearest port. The Captain said that he would do no such thing. His orders were to proceed to Cape Town and Cape Town it was going to be.

'Just keep your eyes peeled for U-boats and I will do the rest,' the Captain told them.

In the meantime the hatch covers came off, and after the Captain and First Mate had a good look round it was decided rather than try and move ammunition and army vehicles, they would pump water to port-side bilge tanks. Although this would leave the ship still with a slight list, it would, barring another storm, see the ship safely to Cape Town.

The cranking steering chain was checked, every link of it, but nothing had weakened. The damage to the engine could only be repaired in port, so the dear old lady limped at four knots all the way to Africa.

The next day O'Dell saw a sight which today would send shudders of horror through the health and hygiene fanatics' departments.

The ice in the cold chamber which held fresh meats and fish had melted away. The Chief Steward and the Cook released the melted ice through the tap, then brought out the last two boxes of fish and about four sides of beef and mutton, all of which stank to high heaven. They then proceeded to wash the slime, mould and fungi off the meats with condi crystals: the purple colour made the meats look even worse. The meats were then cooked and served to everyone from the Captain down.

The Chief Steward told everyone it was their last chance of fresh meat until the ship hit port, so they had better make the most of it. From now on it was to be only salt beef, pork or mutton, or tinned corned beef and only salt fish.

Years later O'Dell was lectured on food safety by two earnest young health officials on the danger of serving meats that had been cooked two days previously and kept in cooling chambers. He thought of the food he and thousands like him had eaten at sea between 1940 and 1945, especially the food served up on the *Llandudno*, but decided not to tell the experts in case it gave them nightmares!

Eat the fish and meat they all did, except for the Third Engineer Officer, who complained the smell made him gag; so the Chief ate his portion.

Life settled down into a shipboard routine. In the afternoons O'Dell was even allowed to spend a couple of hours on the wheel, learning to steer. He was in his element and so happy. Some evenings he helped the Third Mate and deck apprentice with their Morse and flags, also the rules of the road, which he had learnt in an abbreviated version at the Naval School.

His rhyme, 'Green to green, red to red perfect safety go ahead. When upon your port is seen a steamer's starboard light of green there is not so much for you to do for green to red keeps clear of you,' went down very well. All that everyone could say was, 'What the hell are you doing in the Catering Staff?'

Other evenings were spent aft on the well deck hatch, where everyone enjoyed a great get-together: deck crew, catering and D.E.M.S. gunners. The time passed with sing-songs, reciting poems, or just yarning, the old-timers telling the youngest some really tall stories which everyone enjoyed.

One sailor had an accordion, another a Jew's harp. They even used to dance the hornpipe on the hatch covers—without a drink on board except the glass of lime juice the Captain made all hands drink every day.

Each day the weather became warmer and the sea smoother, and by the time Saturday's 'Make and Mend' came around the storm was already fading from his thoughts.

'Make and Mend' was an old seafaring tradition. Everyone except those on watch just relaxed and had a half day off duty. It was a throw back to the old sailing ship days when the old shell backs were given time off to repair canvas shoes, belts, or any clothing torn on deck while working the sails.

O'Dell thought McSally was pulling his leg when he said the Captain would be having a bath next day: there was no running water and he had never seen a bath.

'How can he have a bath?' O'Dell asked.

McSally laughed. 'Wait until tomorrow, Titch. Everyone has to join in,' was all he would say.

The next day at breakfast the Chief told O'Dell that he would be part of the chain gang for the Captain's bath. He looked at the Chief in surprise.

The Chief smiled at the look on O'Dell's face and said, 'It's like this boyo! The engineers heat the water, salt and distilled, by putting steam pipes in the bucket of water. Once the water is boiling, they pass the buckets to the firemen who are spaced out from the bottom to top of the engine room.

'Once the water buckets reach the top, the galley boy, with you and the deck apprentices, pass the buckets along to the Bosun, Chippy and the deck crew who are spaced out along the deck. Then the two officer's boys and the Chief Steward carry them along to the bath.

115

The Captain has to sit in the bath all the time because the bath has a crack in it, look you, which he covers with his arse.'

O'Dell tried to suppress his laughter, but when he looked at the Chief, grinning from ear to ear, he just exploded!

The thought of the Captain blocking a crack with his big bum was just too hilarious. He could not stop laughing.

When he eventually did stop, with tears streaming down his face, he found the Engineers had joined in, and when the Chief added with a straight face, 'But he does take his epaulettes off bach.' O'Dell exploded again.

Even Popeye was swinging and squawking 'Silly old bugger' right on cue. So the day ended with everyone in high spirits over the Captain's bath.

Years later O'Dell realised the Captain was a psychologist before his time. He knew everyone would be talking about his bath for at least two days before the event and for about a week afterwards. In this way he managed to take their minds off other things, like food, heat and U-boats.

In the meantime it now became safe to use the lavatories and they were able to climb up on the throne without getting wet. The sea being calm, only the movement of the ship through the water pushed the sea far enough up the pipe to keep it clean.

The ship was getting very hot inside for sleeping. There was no air conditioning or fans, just a wind scoop made from an oil drum cut in half and put in the porthole in the hope of catching some wind that was not there.

O'Dell found early on that once a steel ship absorbs the heat it stays there until returning to the Atlantic.

One morning Abdul arrived with a home-made hammock, beautifully made of strong canvas with very strong cords each end.

Abdul grinned and said, 'For you. Chief think maybe you like sleep on deck.'

Abdul took O'Dell aft and slung the hammock over the firemen's quarters under the gun platform.

'This your place so that I know where to call you in the mornings.'

He was so grateful, he just didn't know what to say, except, 'Thank you! Oh, thank you, Abdul!'

'That O.K.' said Abdul. 'Remember to lock it up safe in port.'

The days became very hot, and one morning O'Dell saw his first flying fish. He was struck by their sheer beauty and rhythm, they seemed to skim and dive as if dancing a ballet around the bows. Unfortunately every now and then one would misjudge, land on the deck and thence to the frying pan.

When the porpoises joined the flying fish, O'Dell spent hours at night watching them wheeling, skimming, dancing in the phosphorescent seas. It was sheer poetry in motion; a great joy to behold, an unrehearsed ballet in and on the sea.

The Chief appeared around this time with five large clay urns, and told O'Dell that from now on, every day, he was to fill the urns with water and hang them in the sun on the boat deck. The theory was that the heat from the sun on the urns cooled the water inside so that the Engineers had a cool drink in the evenings after a hard hot day in the engine room.

To O'Dell's amazement it worked. The hotter the sun, the cooler the water.

By this time the flour became so thick with weevils and other things that the catering staff had to assist the Cook to sieve it for an hour each day, for the next day's use.

The Chief thought it a waste of time.

'Just call it currant bread,' he advised the Cook.

After three weeks at the rate of four knots, supplies started to get short. There were no potatoes, dried beans or eggs left. Water was rationed, and the pump had a lock put on it.

Everyone still got their half mug of lime juice every day.

Washing of clothes, themselves or water for shaving had to be done with salt water, collected in a bucket from over the ship's side, and there were ropes tied to the rails aft for just that purpose. The Engineers got around the water problem for their urns by using distilled water.

The food situation got worse, the ship ran out of flour, dried and tinned vegetables, tinned Carnation milk, and all cereals.

On the fifth week the ship had no more salt beef, pork, or fish. The only food left was rice (full of weevils), tinned corned beef, Spam, Battle-axe tins of jam, marmalade, butter encased in salt, and curry powder. The Cook really used his imagination. He produced corned beef and rice: boiled, fried curried, baked and made into pies, the crust being hard tack biscuits, crushed and soaked.

The ship moving so slowly and the food situation getting so bad, the Captain decided to head for Walvis Bay, South West Africa.

During the sixth week after the storm the *Llandudno* arrived off Walvis Bay. How marvellous the land looked! The ship had been at sea just on eight weeks.

As the *Llandudno* approached Walvis Bay, a frigate came out to meet and challenge her. Lamping, she asked the ship's name and code number which was of course obsolete by now. The frigate ordered her to hove to, as she circled round and round the *Llandudno*, at the same time keeping a good distance away, with her guns trained on the *Llandudno*.

The Captain was getting madder and madder at the delay.

Eventually the frigate launched a boat, informing the *Llandudno* that a boarding party was on its way and to lower a ladder. It appeared that there was a German raider in the area, using all kinds of disguises to lure the Navy ships near enough to torpedo them. Hence the extra precaution by the frigate.

The *Llandudno* proceeded into harbour with the frigate as escort, and went to anchorage.

Food was sent out to the ship immediately, and the Port Health Doctor came on board. After examining all hands he gave the ship a clean bill of health, but recommended fumigation at Cape Town.

The Cook soon had a meal prepared, and all hands had steak, eggs, bacon and chips galore, lots of fresh shore bread, and real butter, plus a lot of fresh fruit. It all tasted marvellous.

The Captain was escorted ashore by the Navy. On his return, he got all the officers and crew together on number three hatch and gave them the latest news. It appeared that the ship had been given up for lost, and next of kin had been informed that the *Llandudno* was missing, presumed sunk. This had now been rectified, and cables were, that very minute, being sent from Cape Town to the Company and the Admiralty, telling them that the *Llandudno* and all her crew were safe and well.

It also appeared that three merchant ships and one trawler escort

118

had turned turtle in the storm. Seven more ships had been sunk by U-boats and German Raiders as they tried to reach South Africa after the storm. The Navy thought the *Llandudno* had been very lucky.

One last thing the Captain told them.

'This morning the U.S.A. finally entered the war on our side, but only because the Japs have given them a bloody nose and wiped out nearly all their fleet at Pearl Harbour.

Those of you who were on board a year ago when we were in America and witnessed the abuse we received from the Irish and Italian American dockers, and saw the placards of 'Washington and Hitler' which were paraded around the ship, while Lindenburgh ranted and raved with Kennedy about what a useless decadent race we are, will know what satisfaction I am getting from this news.'

In the get-together on the aft hatch that evening the talk countered around the *Llandudno's* survival, and the U.S.A. entering the war. The agreement was 'Good for the Japs! If they had not hit the Yanks, the Yanks would still be sitting on the fence, making money out of us.' O'Dell asked the Bosun what this meant.

'Well, Titch, when we went to war, America was still in the grip of a terrible depression, with thousands of people queuing on the bread line, thousands on free soup, bread in what they called soup kitchens. We suckers going to war cured their unemployment overnight. They opened hundred of factories to make ammunitions and guns of every description, tanks, airplanes and, of course, ships. Being neutral, they offered these for sale to any nation at treble the market price, plus their wheat, oil and other commodities, all at exorbitant prices.'

It was the concensus of opinion among the crew that the Bosun had given a fair comment, or, as one of the A.B.s said, 'You have hit the nail on the head Bose.'

O'Dell discovered the next day that all the Engineer Officers felt exactly the same way.

Some Allies!

The Chief pointed out that Britain had been on its own since Dunkirk; that the Yanks could have come to help but that they were too busy making money out of the situation.

'Don't you ever forget that, Boyo! Forget the bullshit they say that they have come in to fight evil. They have come in because the Japs hit them.'

Two days later, with two other ships and the frigate for escort, they sailed for Cape Town.

O'Dell was to sail to Walvis Bay many times in his sea career, but he never forgot the first time there.

Arriving off Cape Town was also a never to be forgotten experience.

Dawn was just breaking. The cloud, known as the Table Cloth, lay over the Table Mountain. O'Dell gasped, open-mouthed at its magnificence and grandeur. It was surely one of the most beautiful sights in the world.

The dockers swarmed on board, had the hatches off, open and cargo moving before the ship had finished tying up. In no time at all the list disappeared, and the dear old lady straightened up.

The Captain gave everyone a half day.

O'Dell drew his four shillings allowance and went ashore.

The first thing he discovered was that he could not walk straight. It was a strange feeling trying to walk on a flat surface after the ship's rolling and pitching.

He was glad to be on his own to explore Cape Town. The other boy ratings wanted to go ashore with the crew, which was fair enough. They were old enough to drink; he was not.

The first call he made was to the 'Mission to Seamen' at Alfred Street. They made him very welcome, for despite the war-time censorship they all seemed to know about the *Llandudno's* lucky escape, and he had a good natter with lads around his own age.

Then he set off with a two penny road map, found Addlerly Street, the Government buildings, museums, and those wonderful gardens.

He caught a bus to the large building that housed the lifts which took sightseers to the top of Table Mountain.

Reaching the top was an eye-opener. He didn't know what he had expected, except a marvellous view, which of course he got.

What was so unexpected was the large variety of wild flowers to be seen. They were like a carpet, or Jacob's coat of many colours: so breathtakingly beautiful as far as the eye could see all over the mountain top. The view and the wonderful display of flowers left him stunned by its majestic beauty.

Once he was back off the mountain he went to the market and bought twelve peaches, a hand of bananas, a small bag of oranges and three large bunches of juicy dark coloured grapes. Then he headed back on board, arriving just as the crew were heading ashore.

He gorged himself on the fruit and made himself sick.

McSally and Travers arrived back and were sick because of drinking too much beer.

So the first night in Cape Town ended with the three of them ill. But at least O'Dell had no bad head in the morning.

Chapter Eleven

Next morning, three very sorry looking boys reported for work. At first, the Chief was angry because he thought O'Dell was ill from booze but, once he realised the reason, he laughed and said, 'First time I have heard of anyone being ill from too much fruit.'

Asking him what he had done with his time ashore, the Chief expressed amazement that he had gone to the top of Table Mountain. 'All the years I have been at sea, boyo, I have never gone up there, what is it like?' he asked. O'Dell explained about the views and the beautiful mass of various coloured flowers stretched out like a carpet. Even the Captain, it turned out, had only been up the mountain once; none of the Engineer Officers had been there so breakfast time was spent explaining all about it. When he had finished, the Third Engineer Officer said, 'You have still not explained why you went up there!'

South Africa was like a wonderful fairy tale. After war weary, grey blackout Britain, it had no blackout, no food rationing, no clothes rationing; everything was so cheap, everyone so friendly and helpful in the shops and, every evening, people would come down to the docks in their cars, pull up alongside the ships, and offer to take anyone that wanted to go to their homes, or the movies, or a pub crawl, even to the opera.

Life was, for a little while, a happy one and one could be forgiven for forgetting the war, even for a short time.

The old *Llandudno* was soon discharged and entered Dry Dock for repairs and fumigation.

All the Officers and crew were taken ashore and put in a hotel while the ship was in the hands of the fumigating company. Even Popeye had to go ashore, though the Third Engineer Officer had expressed the hope that the damn parrot would also be fumigated, a wish that did not go down well with the Chief and some bitter, heated words were exchanged.

The Cook and galley boy, being black, had to be booked into a different hotel.

This, O'Dell's first experience in relation to a person's colour, left him with a feeling of disquiet. He was taken aback that the crew not only seemed to expect it but even accepted it.

Even the Bosun, when he tentatively raised the subject, said, 'Christ, Titch, grow up, they're bloody black, aren't they.'

Over the years he had the Empire, and what Britain had done for those unfortunate enough not to be born British, rammed down his throat (especially on Empire Day).

He found the experience left a bad taste in his mouth, made worse by the fact that the galley boy and himself did not exactly hit it off.

Being ordered to report back onboard at 1700hrs, after a very large breakfast in which he was introduced to 'Paw Paw', he took himself off to the Museum and the first class library. Borrowing some books on the history of South Africa, he spent the rest of his free time, laying and reading in the glorious sunshine, on the carpet of wild flowers at the top of Table Mountain. Arriving back on board, the first thing noticed by everyone were the three foot high pile after pile of dead cockroaches, thousands of them, and large containers full of dead rats. It was a funny experience walking into the Engineers' saloon and pantry and not seeing cockroaches everywhere, but they were all back in three weeks.

Popeye was back onboard, cackling away and shouting 'Silly old bugger' and, of course, dropping her business all over the place.

On Christmas Eve, the old *Llandudno* left the Dry Dock, her engine repaired, life boats replaced and portside wing of the bridge, and sandbags renewed.

Only the 4.5 gun on the aft platform remained, its breech block still embedded in the platform, with its barrel pointing so forlornly up into the sky, while the large coil spring could still be observed in the split casing getting more and more rusty; it appeared there was not a replacement to be had in Cape Town.

There was also no replacement for the D.E.M.S. Petty Officer, 'Stripey', who was ordered to remain onboard, much to his disgust.

Later, he attended Midnight Mass at the Mission to Seamen, Alfred Street, more as a favour to the Padre than any beliefs.

Christmas Day dawned and, at 0500hrs, he stood on the deck as the sun rose over the Table Mountain; the covering mist, or Table

Cloth, seemed so white and pure. He felt it must surely be one of the greatest sights in the world.

He was to spend many Christmases at sea in his thirty five years on the ocean, but none ever took the place of that first. Everyone had a good Christmas dinner; the Mates and the Engineer Officers serving the crew (who were still half drunk). The Captain and Chief Engineer Officer served the Catering staff and Radio Operators in the Deck Saloon, under the bridge.

A great day with very happy memories and, for a short time, one could forget the war and all its misery.

Sailing day came and the *Llandudno* cleared for sea, now in ballast (except for bags of mail for the island of St. Helena).

Proceeding out from dock, the gun aft caused some ribald comment from the other ships as the *Llandudno* eased her way out, from, 'God, you will frighten every Raider and U-boat around,' to 'Are you going duck shooting?'

The Captain was bouncing with rage on the bridge.

Once clear of the breakwater, the *Llandudno* started to really pitch and roll; she had hit what the seafarers call the famous Cape Rollers and roll she certainly did.

Eventually, the ship lay off St. Helena. Three wooden boats came out manned by the largest well built men he had ever seen, they needed to be as they strained and heaved, their muscles bulging as they fought to get their boats alongside in the offshore swell.

At last, the mail was lowered into their boats and, with big smiles and waves from the boats' crews, the *Llandudno* moved back out to deep sea and turned her nose towards South America.

At the great speed of nine knots, the *Llandudno* was to make a dash for the port of Montevideo, Uruguay.

Her mission—to collect thousands of cases of tinned corn beef to feed the troops in North Africa.

Each ship, heading to South America from South Africa, had to leave at twenty four hour intervals and were not allowed to break radio silence unless attacked by a Raider or U-boat.

So, with no escort, no help and no convoy, the *Llandudno* made her way to South America.

Once again, she was lucky. The King Line ship that had left twenty four hours before her and the Houlder Line ship that had sailed twenty four hours after her, were both sunk by a Raider. Both managed to get a radio message off before sinking.

As soon as the news of the King Line ship came through, the Captain changed course, with a plea to the Chief to try to squeeze another knot out of his engines.

The Chief tried, and actually made twelve knots for two hours, then he had to inform the Captain that, if the ship did not slow up, the poor old 1912 engine would either blow up or seize up. The Captain agreed to ease up and the *Llandudno*, with a big discernible sigh, went back to nine knots.

While everyone, off or on watch, strained their eyeballs looking for the Raider, the tension on the ship for the next few hours was intense.

News from the Houlder Line ship brought a selfish feeling of relief that, at least for the present period, the *Llandudno* had slipped past the Raider.

The only tension left onboard was between the Chief Engineer Officer and Popeye; things had gone from bad to worse in the Engineers' Saloon; it was as if Popeye sensed the Third disliked him so he made the Third's bald head, or his food, his target whenever a meal was in progress.

The Third appealed to the Chief over and over again, to no avail. The sweltering heat did not help as it made Popeye smell even stronger.

One day the Third went berserk, throwing his plate, tea mug, and the tureen full of potatoes.

He missed as Popeye swung along his wires, squawking 'Silly old bugger,' at which the Third threw the tureen full of vegetables.

The Chief roared with rage and threw the Third out into the alleyway; the Third went to see the Captain.

After a long discussion with all the Engineer Officers, from the Chief to the Fourth, the Captain got an agreement with the Chief that Popeye be kept in his cage at meal times—things were never to be the same again between the Chief and his Third Engineer Officer.

Around this time, the ritual of the last of the fresh meat, fish and the condi crystal was performed; seeing the slime and fungi being washed off the meat had been too much for him the second time around, so the Chief ate his portion and he got the Chief's portion of B.O.T. Duff for two weeks.

Around this period, things came to a head between the galley boy and himself.

The galley boy had, from the start, been needling him. At first, he had taken it because the rest of the crew were also taking the mickey, with shouts of, 'Yes Sir, No Sir, lets hear you bang your foot down Titch,' and 'Attention!' being part and parcel of life; no one meant any viciousness, it was just the M.N. way of pulling a new boy's leg and, after the storm, it had died away. The galley boy was different, he kept needling and added his own brand of humour.

Since the South African experience, his malicious remarks had become more personal, even a remark about little bastards being thrown into homes because they had no parents. Travers asked him why he did not belt the galley boy but he had shrugged his shoulders and laughed it off.

One day, the Chief called him into the saloon, sat him down with the other Engineer Officers present, and said, 'Now listen, boyo, we don't like that little black bastard in the galley calling our Mess boy a bastard. Why don't you shut his mouth, look you, you're not frightened of him are you, bach?'

'No Chief,' he replied, 'but one of the things the House Master at Cardiff told me the night before I joined this ship was that 'Ship's Captains' consider fights among crew members one of the worst offences at sea.'

'That's true, boyo, but that does not mean you have to take the shit that the galley boy keeps handing out,' replied the Chief. 'Everyone onboard will reach the conclusion you're a coward if you don't do something,' the Chief continued.

He had felt himself blushing and, for the first time since joining the ship, felt his anger starting to rise at the thought that anyone should think him a coward.

Without a word, he left the Engineers' Saloon and went to the galley. Looking in, he said to the galley boy, 'You, out on deck, before I come and drag you out.'

126

He heard the Cook say, 'get over there and give that little navy whitey a good going over.'

The galley boy came out in a rush, trying to land a head butt, but he had been waiting for it, dropped his head, and the galley boy's nose smashed on the hard top of his head. The fight began in earnest. The galley boy, having been brought up in the Tiger Bay area of Cardiff, knew a trick or two but, as he had been brought up with hundreds of boys, he knew a few himself. Every time he knocked the galley boy down, he let him get up, although all the crew that were off duty and had arrived to watch, kept begging him to put the boot in. It was not until the galley boy tried to boot him that he really saw red and his black monkey took over. With a roar, he really let loose and knew no more until the Chief was pulling him off. As he came out of his black tunnel to the light, he heard the Chief saying, 'that's enough, boyo, you're killing him.'

The poor galley boy was off work for two days and the Chief had made him help out in the Galley until the galley boy was fit for duty.

The ship continued on its way and the daily routine with the hot weather lulled everyone into a false sense of safety until, one morning, smoke was seen on the horizon. Not knowing what ship was making the smoke, a Raider or a friend, the Captain ordered a change of course and again begged the Chief to do his best to squeeze more speed out of his engine.

The *Llandudno* was no match for the other vessel, which was closing fast. Everyone was full of apprehension until the visitor started lamping; she was a Blue Star Line vessel, on her way to South Africa, with a cargo of frozen meat from South America—a deep feeling of relief could be felt right through the *Llandudno*.

As the ship sailed past, the crew asked him what she was lamping. He was able to read the message informing the *Llandudno* there was a Raider about, which had sunk a ship only sixty miles ahead, and wishing the *Llandudno* good luck. As the B.S. Liner disappeared over the horizon, the crew on the *Llandudno* felt apprehensive and vulnerable on the wide ocean. The Captain called those off watch to the deck below the bridge, gave a lecture about getting slack, keeping a good look out at all times and not to relax for one moment.

Next day was his sixteenth birthday. The Chief gave him a day off so he stayed in his hammock until 0800hrs, then went to the galley and was given an egg for his birthday breakfast. The rest of the morning was spent up on the bows reading and the afternoon was spent on the helm, where he was thrilled to be allowed to steer the ship from 1300hrs until 1600hrs; he could not remember being so happy since his days at Suffolk, not even entering the Naval School had he been this happy.

That evening, on the aft hatch, they had sung, 'Happy Birthday, Titch,' and he had recited his two favourite poems—Kipling's 'I vow to you My Country' and 'Psalm of Life' by W.W. Proctor. As he lay in his hammock that night, his thoughts returned to the happy period of his life, when he had lived in Suffolk.

Although he tried to fight them, hot tears came into his eyes as he recalled the love, joy and happiness the Stophers had surrounded him with from day one.

He and his sister had left the G.V. home and were sent to London for a week. They then boarded a train with other boys and girls from the Homes and set off on a journey from London, through Essex— some boys and girls were dropped at each station of call—then on through Suffolk—some being dropped off at Ipswich, Stowmarket and Bacton.

Bacton turned out to be the station for a lot of villages in the area, one of which was called Finningham.

At Bacton Station, the lady in charge from the Homes handed them over to a lady, saying, 'This is the brother and sister you are expecting. As you can see by the label tied to their coat lapel, they are called O'Dell.'

Thus his sister and himself met the lady who was to become the greatest influence of their lives.

As the train pulled out of Bacton Station, the lady, who had introduced herself as Mrs Stopher said, 'Come along. I have a pony and trap outside.' She looked stern and seemed to talk sharp and he instinctively caught hold of his sister's hand; his sister gave a squeeze and quick smile as if to say it's O.K. I am here. Mrs Stopher took hold of his standard blue kit bag, asking his sister if she could manage her own. On receiving an affirmative, she proceeded to lead the way out of the station and into the pony and trap.

They had never rode in a trap before and, for him and his sister, it was a great thrill. On reaching the crossroads at the 'White Horse', Finningham, Mrs Stopher turned right and stopped at the little Post Office-come-General Store. Tying up the pony, she took them into the store and told them to pick some sweets. He had found her voice sharp and, with the Suffolk accent, hard to understand but, when eventually he did understand, he could not belief his ears—he looked at his sister and started to cry, she had to put her arms around him as she explained to Mrs Stopher he was tired and her kind offer of sweets was something new to them. Mrs Stopher became quite upset herself and kept saying, in a broad Suffolk accent, 'poor little lad, poor little lad.'

They left the shop clutching a bag of red aniseed balls in their hands, got back into the trap, back to the crossroads and up Westhorpe Road. He had fallen asleep in his sister's arms by the time they had arrived at the Stophers' farm.

Mr Stopher came out to meet them, lifted him out of his sister's arms and proceeded to carry him indoors. When he opened his eyes and found himself in the arms of this giant, he screamed for his sister so loudly that Mr Stopher nearly dropped him for, although Mrs Stopher was hardly five feet tall, her husband was a good six foot two inches and, as the saying goes, as broad as a barn door.

Mrs Stopher had put him straight to bed and allowed his sister to stay with him. What a bed!!! A large four-poster with a very thick feather mattress and six feather pillows and, clutching tight hold of his sister's hand, he fell straight to sleep. Later, having lit the oil lamps, Mrs Stopher brought a bowl of hot home-made broth and home-made bread—he had never tasted anything like it.

Dawn broke and he found his sister had stayed with him all night. He looked around the room and could not believe the size of it and the beautiful wallpaper.

He heard a lot of cockerels crowing and cows lowing. He got out of bed, found the pot, then went to the windows to have a peep through the curtains—what a beautiful sight, what marvellous countryside.

He heard a movement behind him as his sister awoke.

Then he heard a gasp of horror. Turning sharply, he followed his sister's pointing fingers and, at first, he did not realise what he was looking at, then the penny dropped; the lovely soft blanket-type sheets were supposed to be a cream colour not red—he must have fallen asleep with a red aniseed ball in his mouth and dribbled during his sleep and the result; the top of the sheets were now red.

Fear went through him—oh no! not a hiding on the first day.

He crawled into his sister's arms and she hushed him and told him not to worry, she would take the blame, but he lay there sick with fear. 'I suppose they will send us back to the Home?' he asked his sister.

'Yes,' she said, 'I suppose they will.'

Mrs Stopher entered the bedroom calling out a cheerful, 'Good morning' as she pulled back the curtains.

His sister had started shouting 'I did it, my brother is not to blame', while he had set up a yell of fear.

Mrs Stopher approached the bed and, in her broad accent, said 'Now what's all this about, then?'

He had covered his head with his arms whilst his sister pointed out the red stains, saying, 'I did it, don't hit my brother, he has been ill and is not very strong.'

Mrs Stopher laughed. 'Is that what all this fuss is about, a few red stains? Bless you, m'dears, bain't nothing that won't wash out' and, at her kind words, my sister joined me in tears. 'Come, come,' said Mrs Stopher, 'please don't cry. As for hitting you, bless you, no one in this house will ever set a finger on either of you, so please stop crying, it upsets me so.' He could not believe his ears!

Mrs Stopher picked him up from the bed, gave him a big hug and kiss, set him on the floor, opened the door, pointed out the bathroom opposite and said, 'You go in there and have a good wash while I have a talk with your sister.'

The bathroom was another eye opener; soap that felt creamy and had a lovely smell, thick soft towels and a coloured bath and wash basin.

Arriving back in the bedroom, he found his sister and Mrs Stopher having a talk. His sister was smiling. 'Oh, Thomas,' she said, 'I feel we shall be so happy here,' and it seemed the most natural thing in the world for him to go straight into the arms of Mrs Stopher.

Breakfast was an eye opener; cereals, bacon, egg, tomato, fried bread, toast and marmalade and as many cups of tea as you wanted, with proper china cups and saucers; no aluminium plates and bowls.

All the time he was to spend with the Stophers, he was to feed like a fighting cock—life was good.

After breakfast, Mr Stopher said, 'Would you like to walk around the farm and meadows with me, Thomas?' He had looked to his sister and she said, 'Go on, Thomas, I will stay and help with the washing up.' He looked again at Mr Stopher; he still looked a giant; he wondered if he was like the one on the beanstalk!! and felt a little afraid. Mrs Stopher seemed to realise he was nervous and said, 'bain't no hurry for the washing up, we shall all go.' To which he nodded and said, 'Oh, yes please.'

The farm was, by farming standards, not too large but, to him, it seemed very large, with hundreds of chickens and ducks, three fields for beetroot and the fourth (called the lower meadow) had a stream running through it with cattle grazing and a large sandpit. This was the field he was to spend so many happy hours in; a large tree blown down lay across the stream and was to become his ship that he would sail around the world on, sometimes as a pirate, sometimes as a navy ship seeking out the pirates; Mr Stopher was to nail planks on the fallen tree for him to walk the deck on.

His giant turned out to be the kindest, gentlest and most wonderful of men and, like his wife, a true Christian in the fullest sense of the word.

Love and warmth poured forth from them both—they were to treat both him and his sister like their own.

It had to be Paradise on earth. The next few days were spent getting to know each other and the farm. The Stophers already had a family of four grownup sons, the youngest being twenty years old, all married and living away from home. They all called to see the new additions to the family and like their parents, were kind and warm in their welcome.

Every Sunday morning, to comply with their agreement with the Home, Mrs Stopher took them to the C. of E. church but Sunday afternoons and evenings were spent at the Chapel.

The Stophers were great Chapel people; even though the Chapel was at least three miles away, they walked there and back in good weather, pony and trap in rain or snow.

He enjoyed every moment; walking down the country lanes

holding Mrs Stopher's hand was sheer joy to him. On the first Sunday, Mrs Stopher pointed out the village school, not far up the lane from the church and, like everywhere else in Finningham, it was a wonderful place. The Head was Mrs Freer, ably supported by Miss Eagle and Miss Horn, who made them so very welcome.

In fact, the whole village of Finningham made them, and all the other boys and girls from the Homes, very welcome and showered them all with love and kindness.

As he lay that night in his hammock, he recalled those glorious Springs, Summers, Autumns and Winters and wondered if he would survive the war to see them all again (he did).

To see the countryside coming alive as they walked to school and back; the masses of primrose, bluebells, cowslips, on the banks each side of the lanes, breaking forth to herald the arrival, once more, of Spring.

The new chicks and ducklings born in their hundreds and helping to put them gently into the boxes as Mr Stopher sold them to the buyer at Stowmarket.

To watch the new born calf at midnight, staggering around as the mother nudged it onto its feet.

The ploughing and the sowing, it really was God's world in seasons. The summer time, with the harvest, the tractor going from farm to farm and the farmers and their farm labourers, moving with the tractor, to help each other in the thrashing, stacking and harvesting of the crop—for all the great depression the whole country was going through, Finningham seemed to let it pass by, helping each other.

Autumn with the first chill in the mornings and the nights closing in, heralded the evening around the piano, while Mrs Stopher played, and hymn after hymn was sung, whilst chestnuts and potatoes roasted around the fire. What bliss!!

By this time, the kindness of the Stophers, and their example, had taught him and his sister there was a kind loving God, also that his temper and rages were not evil but a black monkey he had to learn to control.

Winter with Mr Jack Frost painting the countryside white in beautiful forms; getting up those mornings, while it was still dark, and helping Mr Stopher clear the frozen water point for the chickens and ducks to be able to have a drink—he used to feel so important—then returning to the farmhouse for a hot full breakfast—how he loved those mornings—before walking to school, the snowstorms which sometimes made all lanes and fields impassable, creating a holiday off school and snowball fights.

The two best times in Winter were, of course, Christmas and the rabbit hunting. The farmers and farm labourers would all start arriving on Saturday at around 1400hrs, about once a month, with their ferrets in sacks and their guns under their arms. At a given time, everyone moved off and the rabbit cull would begin; ferrets put down the rabbit holes, guns blasting off, as the rabbits tried to escape from their back holes.

He always had to keep at Mr Stopher's side if he did not, he was not allowed to join the next rabbit cull.

It was the end he liked best. As dusk started to fall, whistles were blown and everyone made their way back to Stophers, to the warm kitchen with its great fire roaring; all the wives and sweethearts would have arrived and prepared the food, the table groaning under the weight and, on the far side, wooden kegs of beer and tankards awaited to be used, although it has to be said, Mrs Stopher was not fussy about having beer in her kitchen. He loved the smell of all the fresh bread, sausage rolls, beef pies, baked tongues and baked hams, also the deep rhubarb pies and deep apple pies.

To listen to everyone talking about weather, harvest, the state of the country, while all the caught rabbits were crossed legged and put on sticks.

He always ended up fast asleep under the table where Mr Stopher would rescue him.

Chapter Twelve

Mr Stopher would rescue him and carry him up to bed—another wonderful day over. Oh! what a wonderful period of his life.

He was to learn, the hard way, that every good period had to be paid for by a bad one.

The Christmas days were also wonderful, with the Church and Chapel services, the early morning visits of Father Christmas and the presents. For the first time in his life, he received more than an apple and orange on Christmas Day. He could still recall that first Christmas morning, awakened by his sister, to see stockings hanging from the bedrail and presents on the floor; the sheer wonder and joy that swept over him. Then, with his sister, Mr and Mrs Stopher came into the bedroom to sing his favourite carol 'In the bleak mid Winter'; after a lot of hugging and tears of happiness, more carols, then breakfast.

After Church and Chapel services, the evening would be spent roasting chestnuts and potatoes around the fire, with Mrs Stopher playing the piano, and the farmhouse alive with carols.

Last thing every Christmas night before bed, he was allowed to stay up and walk around the farm with Mr Stopher checking his flocks of chicken, ducks and cattle in the lower meadow; he was usually asleep before they had finished the rounds and Mr Stopher would carry him home on his shoulder.

The only sad part of life in Suffolk was his sister's return to the home, to be sent out to service at some big house. He had been upset at first, but his sister pointed out that they had been lucky to have a year together and to 'Thank God' that at least we had been lucky enough to find a home with wonderful people like the Stophers.

When one is young, logic does not come into it. He felt so unhappy; his sister had been everything to him, his protector, best friend, his link to his birth.

A few days after his sister departed, Mr Stopher gave him a plot of land to grow whatever he wished, flowers, vegetables, whatever. After Mr Stopher had shown him how to double trench the plot, he planted the border with primroses, a flower he had come to associate with happiness and which was to be his favourite for the rest of his life.

The fresh air, food and the Stophers' kindness was paying off, he grew fitter, healthier, putting a lot of weight on his body. He was certainly different from the sickly child that had arrived over a year ago, even his tantrums had become less frequent. The years passed by and time flew; the memories of the Homes faded away and he could only remember his sister clearly.

The jubilee came and the whole village celebrated in the village school and, for the first time in his life, he saw people drunk, much to Mrs Stopher's disgust.

Not long after the Jubilee celebrations, disaster struck, Mrs Stopher had a heart attack. She lay in her bed so deathly white and, as he sat beside her, he prayed and prayed as he had never done before, pleading with God not to take this angel on earth away to be an angel in heaven; he would not leave her side until Mr Stopher took over. At night, he knelt on his knees and begged God not to take her away; he stayed on his knees until there was no feeling, just praying and praying and talking—he was never again to feel so close to God. In the morning, Mr Stopher found him asleep still on his knees.

Mrs Stopher recovered but was never to have the same strength again, but at least she was alive; he and Mr Stopher took over any hard work.

That same year, the local Doctor had a visitor staying with him from Germany. Memories die hard in a small country village; soon the whole village was up in arms, not only because the Doctor should be friendly with the filthy Hun, but they were incensed that he had invited the Hun in November; tempers got so out of hand that a policeman was sent from Stowmarket to read the riot act to the villagers outside the 'White Horse'.

On Armistice Day, tempers again ran high, especially at 1100hrs, after everyone had stood for two minutes silence to honour those who had left Finningham, 1914 to 1918, and never returned.

That night, some of the men, after a few drinks at the 'White Horse', marched on the Doctor's house; half were armed with pitchforks, others with large sticks and stones. They were met halfway up the long drive by the Doctor, who explained that he and the Hun belonged to an organisation trying to cement friendship between

135

Germany and England. After a lot of debate and raised voices, the men dispersed, but bad feeling between the Doctor and some of the veterans remained for a time.

Who would have thought that night that, in four years, half of those men would be manning a position in the village, armed only with pitchforks, to repel a German airborne attack, while the other half were in Singapore fighting the Japs.

Not long after, the King died. A visitor arrived from the Homes and she asked him what he wanted to be in life. He told her he wished to stay with the Stophers and, when he left school, to work on the farm. She informed him that this was not possible and, gave him the following choices—go to Canada or Australia and work on a farm, go to a Naval School and then to sea, or become a printer at Tunbridge Wells. He decided on the Naval School.

The visitor left, informing the Stophers they would hear from the Homes when I would be leaving for the Naval School.

Life went on, months flew by and his tantrums or, as Mrs Stopher called them, his little black monkeys, faded away.

Around this time, he was to experience another of those peculiar events that seemed to happen to him every so often.

He had been at his plot of land pulling up carrots when, all of a sudden, he was engulfed in a loud sound of shouting and clashing of swords and steel. Although frightened, he was also fascinated as the men seemed to whirl around him: it was the first time he had ever seen men in kilts. All of a sudden, a man appeared in front of him, sword in hand, wearing a kilt. He said one word 'Courage' then everything disappeared as fast as it had arrived. It could only have lasted for a few moments but everything was so loud and clear. He rushed into the farmhouse to tell Mrs Stopher but she thought he had fallen asleep and dreamt it.

A few weeks later, they received word from the Homes saying what day he was to be ready to leave for the Naval School.

As the day drew near for him to leave, he became unhappy for although he wanted to go to sea, the love he bore the Stophers was as strong as any son for his parents, they meant the whole world to him and he could not imagine life without them. He loved them dearly and owed them so much.

The morning of parting was spent in prayer and tears, then off in the pony and trap to Bacton Station, where it had all started nearly five years before.

The weak, sickly child was now a strong, thick set, though still stunted, boy and as brown as a nut.

Mrs Stopher was now a sick, ageing lady, who he worshipped.

The train arrived, the woman from the Homes stepped off the train and took over. 'Right O'Dell, pick up your kit bag and get on the train.'

Mrs Stopher gave him a hug and a gentle smile, 'Go Thomas, and God go with you.'

On the train, he discovered four other boys who had been collected along the way and they moved up so that he could sit near the window to wave goodbye.

He tried so hard to stop the tears as the train pulled out of Bacton Station, but they flowed down his face. The woman from the Homes said, 'that's enough of that, O'Dell, if you're going to the Naval School, you had better start acting as a man.' He looked at the other boys in the compartment and could see that they had all had a weep; somehow, that made him feel better.

Youth is resilient and, in no time, they were all chatting away, discovering in which village they had been boarded out.

At Ipswich, a young man got into the compartment. He looked about the same age as the woman from the Homes and, in a short time, they introduced themselves, the woman from the Homes telling him about her job and us, her charges.

He asked each of them individually where they were born and how long they had been in the Homes.

When it was his turn he answered 'Belfast.'

'Oh!' said the young man.

'Yes,' he had replied 'but not the filthy IRA.'

'That will be enough of that O'Dell,' said the woman from the Homes sharply.

The young man had laughed, 'and what do you know about the IRA at your young age?'

He told him about the friend of the Stophers, a Postman, killed by a bomb on opening a postbox to collect mail in London. All the time, the woman from the Homes was trying to shut him up but, he had been away from the Homes too long, to see and hear the warning signs, he just kept talking to the young man.

He was completely unaware, having tasted the freedom in Suffolk, that his period of rehabilitation for institutional life was about to descend on him with all its night.

On arriving in London, the boys were split up, three going on to the HQ, while he and another boy were taken, by the same woman on the train, to a transit house.

Arriving there, she left them in the foyer with strict orders not to talk to anyone, while she went to the Matron's Office.

After a while, she and the Matron came out of the Office.

'You, O'Dell,' said the woman from the train, 'into the office now.'

He went in, the woman following and, turning him around, she hit him hard across the face, he staggered back from the force of the blow; he was completely bewildered and cried out in shock and pain: she hit him again on the other side of his face.

'Remember, next time you are told to stop talking and to sit down, you do it right away,' she continued, 'it's a good job I am not staying, I would soon bring you into line.' With that, she left, saying to the Matron, 'he is all yours.'

He stood there shocked, dismayed, fearful and utterly disoriented. He had not been hit for nearly five years. All of a sudden, he felt overwhelmed, in sheer panic and despair — Oh God! what was going to happen to him now?

The Matron showed them to their dormitory and he felt a sinking feeling as memories flooded back, hard mattress and pillows, stiff white sheets; he thought of the luxury of his own feather bed, his own room, even his own hand-picked wall paper. He stifled a sob that arose in his throat and gritted his teeth as he stowed his gear in the tin trunk allotted to him.

On the way down, he asked the Matron when he would be leaving for the Naval School.

The Matron stopped. 'Boy,' she said, 'you don't speak until you are given permission, is that clear?' He had nodded an affirmative.

'Good,' she continued, 'if you are smart, do what you are told and obey all the rules, you will save yourself a lot of grief, try and make your three weeks transit period as easy on yourself as you can.' Once downstairs, they were sent into a room where all the boys were at assembly, waiting to go in for evening tea.

He joined the end of the line and along the line came a hunchback with large horn-rimmed glasses. On reaching him she stopped, malevolence oozed out of her, and she said, 'this is the new pretty boy with the big mouth I have been hearing about.' She took hold of his curly hair roughly in her left hand, shaking his head from side to side, and said 'We will have this off tomorrow, pretty boy', increasing the rough pressure and pulling harder. He had yelled at her to leave him alone; she hit him, the lump on her back swaying as she screamed 'Who gave you permission to talk, pretty boy?' Spittle from her mouth covered his face, her head and lump going up and down in her frenzy. Ordering the other boys into the dining room, she left him standing there, full of apprehension and a gut feeling of terror. He did not have long to wait; shuffling along like all hunchbacks, she came up to him, hissing 'No food for you tonight, pretty boy.'

He look at her with utter contempt.

He saw the hatred in her eyes as she hit him, screaming 'Don't give me any dumb insolence.' The force of the blow knocked him down and, as he slipped on the polished floor, hitting his head on an old iron radiator, his black monkey took over. With a yell, he got up and charged but the hunchback was waiting. Grabbing his hair with one hand, she belted him with the other, her strength was an eye opener and, as he fell down, he vomited.

The hunchback left him laying there.

On her return, she had a bucket of water which she threw over the vomit then, putting a cloth in his hands ordered him to mop it up on his hands and knees. Sobbing, vomit still in his mouth and nose, dazed and completely numb, he mopped it up.

When he had finished, the hunchback threw ronuck all over the floor and ordered him to rub it in, giving him another belt around the head to encourage him to move faster.

He could not believe what was happening to him, only that morning he had been in Suffolk, enclosed in love and joy; this evening he was receiving this treatment, it was as if his world had gone mad.

Giving him another cloth, he was ordered to polish the floor. While he moved up and down the room on his knees, polishing, the hunchback sat on a chair needling and tormenting him, 'So you thought you were going to the Naval School, pretty boy? No chance, no one from here ever goes to the Naval School, they don't want the likes of you, only real men, pretty boy.'

Her words penetrated through his despair, he felt a great betrayal as if everyone had let him down.

He was never to remember how that night ended, nor to remember how the three weeks in the transit home passed; his mind went a complete blank, never to be aware of any of that period.

It was to be such a psychological trauma that he was never again able to trust anyone completely.

When his brain started to register what was going on, he was already in the Boys' City.

The city was well run by a retired Naval Captain, all Masters and Matrons being answerable to him. The Captain, R.N. Rtd., lived in a large country house with his servants, the house being situated in the middle of a large lawn and woe betide any boy putting a foot on that immaculate lawn.

Discipline was strict, as indeed it had to be with eight hundred boys, but it was fair. All houses in the Boys' City were called after places in Britain or the Empire. He was put in a house called 'Union Jack' run by a Matron called Mrs Mansfield, who was a kind but firm lady.

He, himself, was unapproachable, snarling at anyone and, after a few fights in his black monkey rages, he was left strictly alone, in fact, he was to earn a reputation of being a little mental.

After a while, Mrs Mansfield sent for him and sat him down in her office, where she produced all the letters he had written to the Stophers accusing them of treachery and betrayal; they were also full of hate and anger and, up to then, he had not been aware that all mail was censored.

Mrs Mansfield pointed out that it was foolish and not logical to blame the Stophers for everything; that when I left Suffolk it was obvious that the Stophers had genuinely thought I was off to the Naval School and would be wondering why they had not heard from me; she pointed out that, instead of blaming the Stophers, I should be thanking them for the happiness they had given to me.

140

When Matron offered him another sheet of paper to write to the Stophers to thank them for everything, he refused it. He was not to write to them until he entered the Naval School.

Life at the city settled into a dull routine and, apart from the sport, he hated every moment of it. Sport saved his reason – he was soon in the boxing, cricket and football teams, yet he was not really ever one of the team, he just could not trust anyone with the slightest feeling of friendship.

He went first to a school called Snakes Lane, then to the new Woodford Secondary run by a retired Army Officer.

It was at Woodford Secondary he met his first Germans.

The Headmaster believed that, if the youth of different countries got together, wars would cease; as an ex Army man, he should have known better. He often wondered how the Head had felt, a year later, when war started; he could still recall the Head's speech about how Germany only wanted peace and no war.

The young Germans, brought over by two adults, were all swagger and strut, their arrogance unbelievable and they kept showing their dirks with the swastika inlaid in the handles. Two of them informed him there would definitely be a war which, this time, they would certainly win; so much for youth meeting youth.

The Homes decided that year to hold the Empire Day celebrations at the Boys' City, with all the other homes sending representatives. The first to arrive was a full band and one squad from the Naval School. For the first time since leaving Suffolk, he became normal and alive; for the five days the Naval School detachment were at the city, he lived and breathed with them, to him they symbolised his ache and hunger.

Even the P.O. in charge got fed up with all his questions. 'For God's sake, Titch, if you want to know so much, come and join us.'

He pointed out that he had tried and tried to no avail.

'Well, keep trying,' snapped the P.O.

Not long after Empire Day, the news swept through the city that all 800 boys were to be taken to a local cinema to see a film called 'Boys from the Homes'.

Acted by Mickey Rooney and Freddie Bartholomew, it was all about our Naval School with its Integrity, Loyalty and Honour.

It was, of course, complete propaganda; Goebbels would have been proud of it but, on the way back from the cinema, he was more determined than ever to get to the Naval School.

It was also the first film he had ever seen.

The following Saturday morning, he was walking past the Captain's famous lawn when the Captain himself came out and started to practice his putt shots and swing his clubs. He stood for a while watching, then he thought, why not give it a try, what had he got to lose, they could not hurt him more than the hunchback had. Plucking up courage, his heart thumping and thumping, he started walking on the famous lawn towards the Captain.

After a few steps, he heard a master shouting 'You boy, off the lawn.'

He kept walking.

He heard the Master shouting 'Off that lawn boy, at once.'

He kept walking.

He looked up and saw the Captain wave the Master to silence.

His heart still racing, he kept walking.

On reaching the Captain, he stood stiffly to attention, beads of perspiration pouring down his face; he thought for a horrid moment that he was going to faint, his chest hurt.

He heard, through his dizziness, the Captain say 'Well, young fellow, that must have taken a great effort. To what do I owe this pleasure?'

He looked up into a pair of very amused twinkling grey eyes. 'I want to go to the Naval School, Sir, and they won't let me,' he blurted out.

'So it's the Navy you want,' said the Captain. 'Well, let me tell you, young fellow, if you walked on my deck at sea without my permission, you would be in deep trouble and, as this lawn is my shore deck, the same thing applies. Now, what's all this about the Naval School?'

He started to tell the Captain about Suffolk, the Naval School and the hunchback.

'Whoa!' said the Captain in a kind voice, 'slow down. First, what is your name. I see your number 109 but what is your name?'

He told him his name. 'Right, O'Dell, sit down on the lawn, start at the beginning and slowly.'

He sat down on the sacred lawn and told the Captain everything from the time he went to Suffolk, the wonderful Stophers, the Homes' promise of the Naval School, the transit house, the hunchback and of his deep unhappiness, his desolate feeling of betrayal.

Ending his tale, his lips started to quiver and it took all his self control not to break down.

He heard the Captain's voice saying 'Well boy, I cannot promise you anything but I will certainly look into it.'

He called Mr Milson, the Master, over. 'The boy is not to be punished by anyone,' the Captain informed him. 'I will decide his punishment when his Matron brings him to see me at 1930hrs Monday.'

As they moved away, the Captain called out 'Don't forget, no one is to punish the boy, Mr Milson.'

On reaching the end of the lawn, Mr Milson said 'Go straight to your home boy and tell Mrs Mansfield the Captain's orders.'

On reporting to Mrs Mansfield, she said 'Oh! O'Dell, whatever will become of you, going on the Captain's lawn.' Her voice held a touch of awe as she mentioned the Captain.

But, at least, no one punished him and all the boys in the 'Union Jack House' looked at him as if he had two heads.

That night, there was a big discussion in the dormitory as to what his punishment would be! 'Don't let them send you to Australia,' said Stan Harvey, 'it's hell out there.'

Harvey had just arrived back from Australia; he was nearly blind and, for all his thick glasses, could only see shadows.

It appeared he had been sent out to a farm in Australia called 'Fairbridge Farm'. Unfortunately for Harvey, the Doctor at H.Q. had failed to notice he had very weak eye sight and the searing hot sun of Australia had nearly finished his sight off.

Someone shouted out 'What is 'Fairbridge Farm' really like, Harvey?'

Harvey sat down and told the dormitory his experiences at the farm; he told them about the terrible heat, flies, and the hard cruel discipline, a regime where everyone worked from 0530hrs until 2000hrs every day, miles from civilisation, and how the senior boys were as cruel as the Masters and Matrons.

He said there was a song they used to sing, which went like this:

There's a river at the back
of the old Garry track,
On the way to Fairbridge Farm,
You will never see a marriage
for over forty years,
You will never see a carriage
for over forty years,
But there is a river at the back
of the old Garry track,
On the way to Fairbridge Farm.

'So, O'Dell,' Harvey concluded, 'make sure the Captain's punishment is not Australia.'

On Monday, at 1915hrs prompt, the Matron took him up the road to the big house. On the way, she advised him to tell the Captain how sorry he was and to ask his forgiveness.

Prompt at 1930hrs, he was marched into the Captain's office, his stomach churning, full of apprehension. The Captain dismissed the Matron, she gave a bob of a curtsey and left.

'Sit down, boy,' said the Captain, indicating to a large chair; he found his legs could not reach the floor.

'Well boy,' continued the Captain, 'I have read your file and been in touch with H.Q. It would appear you have a history of blind rages and are a suspect for epilepsy. Do you understand what that means?'

He shook his head and said in a quivering voice, 'No, Sir.'

'But you admit to the blind rages?'

'Oh yes, Sir. One Matron called it the Evil Devil, the Stophers called it my black monkey and the Assistant Matron at the transit house claimed it was because I was a rat, but I have never heard it called the name you mentioned, Sir.'

'Ahem! Well, we will come back to the transit house in a moment. Firstly, O'Dell, tell me what triggers these blind rage attacks?'

'Well, if someone hits me hard, or I am frustrated, Sir, then I just see a red flash, then I don't remember anything until I am coming out of a long dark tunnel with a light at the end.'

'Sounds to me that you want to learn self control, boy,' said the Captain, 'and the Navy is the best place for that.'

The Captain continued 'Well, O'Dell, with the H.Q. agreement, you will be examined by a specialist Doctor. If all goes well, I will secure you a place in the Naval School; if you are an epilepsy suspect, you will remain here. In the meantime, you will not be allowed to play in the boxing, football or gym display teams. Is that clear?'

'Yes, Sir.'

'Now, as to the transit house business, do you still maintain you were beaten up, made to wipe your vomit up and polish the floor, and suffered continuous abuse? Think hard before you answer, O'Dell, I want the truth.'

'If verbal abuse means being shouted at and called names, yes Sir.'

He could still recall the Captain looking at him for what seemed a long time, then he said, 'So be it, O'Dell, you're dismissed.'

The Captain pressed a bell on his desk. When the Matron came in, the Captain said 'Mrs Mansfield, this boy will be seeing a Doctor. If all goes well, the Navy will have him.'

On the way back, the Matron asked him what the Captain had said or done. He replied that he had strict orders not to repeat anything that passed between them.

'Quite right, too,' said the Matron.

In six weeks he entered the Naval School.

At an early age, he learnt the true lesson of life – if you really want something, go to the top.

As far as the hunchback was concerned, he had to wait until the 1970s for his revenge.

Chapter Thirteen

The sound of the ship's bell, announcing the end of the watch, broke through his reminiscence. With a start, he realised it also meant the end of the day and, with it, the end of his happy sixteenth birthday. He heard the watch call out to the Second Mate on the bridge that they had been relieved and, with a happy sigh, drifted off to sleep.

A few days later, after having gone through the now familiar Captain's bath routine, land was spotted on the starboard bow; South American landfall had been reached.

Next morning, a Uruguay gunboat came out to welcome them and to assure them they were safe in Uruguay Territorial Waters. As they approached the Port of Montevideo, the superstructure of the famous pocket battleship 'Graf Spee' could still be seen above the waterline as she slowly sunk in the mud of the River Plate.

The Captain ordered the Red Duster to be broken out aft, with a sailor standing by to dip it as the ship moved slowly past the 'Graf Spee'; the D.E.M.S. Gunners, under Stripey, stood to attention facing outward on the starboard side.

O'Dell had always had great respect for the Captain but as they slipped past the burnout Graf Spee', with it's gaping large holes left by the heavy guns of the British Navy, he felt admiration that the Captain had shown such respect to an enemy that had put up a good fight and had flown the old German Battle Ensign, with no Nazi Flag in sight, as she blew herself up, although, it has to be said, not everyone on board felt the same. Some of the crew felt saluting the 'Graf Spee' was an insult to the British dead. Stripey defended the D.E.M.S. Gunners by pointing out it was tradition.

The Pilot came out to take the Llandudno to her berth.

To the great surprise of the whole ship's Officers and crew, the people of Montevideo had turned out in force to welcome them. If the people of Montevideo felt let down that the British ship they were waiting to welcome turned out to be a very old, rusty Welsh Tramp Steamer, they gave no sign of it as they waved flags (British and Uruguay) and cheered and cheered, with two small bands each playing different tunes at the same time. Once the Llandudno was warped alongside and the gangway out, the crowd parted to let everyone on the ship see that they had painted a very large 'Union Jack' on the dockside.

No welcome could have been more generous or sincere. With the crowds swarming on board, the Captain and the Ship's Agent soon realised there would be no work done by the dockers that day. The whole ship was invaded; there were people milling around from the bow to the stern. Laughing, talking, smiling, they covered every part of the ship, even the engine room.

Young girls, with their dark flashing eyes and their chaperons, giggled and hid behind lovely coloured fans as they inched past. All the young men seemed to head for the poor old 4.5 gun on the aft platform, its barrel still pointing up in the air. They were convinced it had been hit by a German shell in battle and the D.E.M.S. Gunners did nothing to dissemble their illusions, especially as most of them had their young sisters in tow. They even invaded the Engineer Officers' Saloon, crowding around and accepting mugs of tea whilst being entertained by Popeye's antics.

After about three hours, and a lot of loud shouting on a hailer, the crowd started to thin out and go ashore, much to the Captain and the Agent's delight.

In the meantime, McSally, Travers and himself tried chatting up some of the young girls. Unfortunately, none could speak English. However, by signs, he had managed to convey to one of the dark-eyed beauties that he would like to meet her ashore. By a lot of miming and laughter, it was agreed he would meet her and the chaperon around 1900hrs; they wrote down the address and off they went – her name was Lydia.

The five days in port soon passed and the Llandudno prepared for sea. He had met Lydia the four nights in port and, although they could not converse, by much signs, miming and giggles and laughter, they had really enjoyed themselves. During their walks in the well lit park and streets of Montevideo, they sometimes held hands but never embraced or kissed.

Travers and McSally thought he was nuts; they were having a wonderful time in the bars and nightclubs. He was happy and contented with his Lydia.

On the last night, Travers begged him to drop Lydia and come with them. 'Look, O'Dell,' he said, 'we might 'buy it' from a U-boat or Raider on the way back to South Africa. Surely, you don't want to die without having a woman!' He had been sorely tempted but felt he could not let Lydia down after her kindness and friendship.

They sailed in the dark. After dropping the Pilot, the Captain set the ship's nose for South Africa.

As dawn broke, the Captain mustered all hands and told them that everyone had to keep their eyes peeled, even more than ever, for any sign of smoke, Raider or U-boat. He explained that their arrival at Montevideo would have been noted by the German Consul and there would be a great effort by the German Navy to stop the 'Llandudno' supplying food to the army in North Africa. 'So,' the Captain ended, 'I want everyone, even if you're not on duty or on watch, if you're on deck, just to go to the heads, to keep your eyes peeled and make sure the ship is completely blacked out at all times.'

After that pep talk, everyone felt a little apprehensive and the first few days found everyone staring out to sea, but it soon wore off.

One thing had come on board at Montevideo which guaranteed there would be no meat washed with condi crystals; that was twelve live sheep, three pigs and two goats – the Llandudno was going to be all right for meat this part of the voyage.

The Captain had been presented with a new cast iron bath by the Ship's Agent in Montevideo. The Chief Engineer Officer had let slip, after a few drinks one evening at the Agent's house, that the Captain had to sit on a crack when he wanted a bath which, apparently, caused great hilarity, much to the Captain's embarrassment, as the Agent explained, in Spanish, to the other guests at the party. It now meant all hands could fill the new bath with the Captain standing watching. Somehow, it was not such an enjoyable chore any more.

After the ice had melted and the frozen meat finished, all hands off watch had an enjoyable time watching the cook and galley boy chasing the sheep, pigs or goats and all agreed the pigs were the star turn. Somehow they gave the cook and galley boy a real hard time, escaping over and over again just as the cook was going to cut their throats. Once, on a very hot day, as No. 2 pig was giving them a hard time with the crew watching, howling with laughter and shouting advice, the cook gave a shout of rage, jumped out of the pigs' pen and charged at the crew waving his large, very sharp knife. Everyone scattered fast and left the cook alone until he had simmered down and started laughing himself.

The days slowly passed and the dear old lady chugged along at her rate of nine knots, South Africa drawing perceptibly nearer each day that passed. One could sense the feeling on the ship that we were going to make it.

At last, the South African coast appeared on the horizon, much to everyone's joy, and the Llandudno made her signal. A Navy frigate came to escort her into port and everyone heaved a sigh of relief. Tonight, in port, they could all sleep with their nerves relaxed without wondering if they would live the night out.

Their arrival in South Africa coincided with the news that the Captain had been awarded the O.B.E., not only for saving his ship and crew in the terrible storm by his wonderful seamanship, but also for saving the very urgently needed cargo of war material that our army needed in North Africa so very badly. So many other ships in the storm had jettisoned their cargo of tanks, ammunitions, bren gun carriers and guns in order to save themselves. Our Captain may have lost his lifeboats and part of the ship's bridge, but not one item of the cargo entrusted to him.

The next day, as he arrived with the Engineer Officers' tea in their saloon, he found the Captain with them. After quickly putting another thick china mug on the table, the Chief said, 'We were just discussing the Captain's award, boyo. We all think he should have received the M.B.E., what do you think, bach?'

He had look around the table and he could tell they were awaiting his reply. 'Why the M.B.E., Chief?' he asked, deciding to go along with the game. 'Well, bach,' said the Chief, grinning, 'the O.B.E. means 'Others' bloody efforts' but the M.B.E. means 'My bloody efforts.' Looking around, he saw the rest of the Engineer Officers, and the Captain, smiling and grinning at their joke.

The following day, the Captain sent for the three boy ratings. He informed them that a Reverend David Plains and his wife Merle had offered to take the three of them out for the evening and would be down to pick them up in their car at 1900hrs.

He was thrilled at the thought of a ride in a car but both Travers and McSally were irked and annoyed that the Captain had made them go with the Reverend and his wife; they wanted to go out on the town with the rest of the crew.

Their hosts arrived; the Captain met them at the gangway and introduced them.

He was to remember that first meeting for the rest of his life. He had heard a lot from the crew about women and, although he had no experience, he had some preconceived ideas but nothing to prepare him for reality. His confined upbringing in the orphanage and Naval School had seen to that.

The Reverend was a tall, dark-haired, handsome man but his wife was the most beautiful woman he had ever seen; every film star faded into nothing. Mrs. Merle Plains was a blonde, blue-eyed, husky voiced goddess and, when she said 'Hello' his heart did a flip as he blushed and stammered to reply.

The couple did everything to put him at ease but whenever Mrs. Plains spoke to him in that exciting husky voice and gave him a slow wonderful smile, he just went tongue tied and blushed, until the Rev. David laughed and said 'Don't upset the boy, Merle.'

It turned out that their parish was on the outskirts of the city along the coast. It was a lovely spot and, sitting on their verandah, you could see and hear the sea as it crashed along the shoreline. It was a wonderful evening and he did not want it to end. He could not get over the way both the parson and his wife spoke and treated him as an equal.

On the way back to the ship, Travers and McSally both said they had enjoyed the evening. and thanked their hosts but, at the same time, made it clear they would not be free the next night – they wanted the bright lights.

He became their one and only visitor and he enjoyed it so very much. After the first evening, the Reverend insisted he called them David and Merle.

As they came out of the 'Playhouse' on the third evening, Merle asked him if he could get off duty the next afternoon as they would like to take him on a picnic. He explained that they would have to ask the Chief Engineer Officer.

Next morning, David came on board early and spoke with the

Chief and, much to his surprise and joy, it was agreed that not only would he be allowed a half day but the whole weekend, from midday Friday until after Evensong Sunday night; he was floating on air.

Prompt at midday, Merle arrived in her car, a sporty M.G. It appeared that some church business had cropped up that David had to attend to.

His heart sank and Merle must have guessed his thought by the look on his face. She laughed that silver bell laugh. 'Don't worry,' she said, 'we are still having our picnic.' They drove out of the docks, he showed his shore pass, and they were off.

Merle said, 'We are not calling home; we will carry on along the coast to a place called Umcumaz. David and I have a small summer cottage there. David will join us later.'

When they reached Umcumaz, Merle drove to a little cove and he was thrilled to see they had it all to themselves, although there were people just around the corner in the next cove. Merle had guessed his size and bought him some royal blue swimming trunks.

Years later, when he joined the Freemasons and everything in his Mother Lodge was covered in royal blue, it brought back vivid memories of those first royal blue swimming trunks.

They started to unload the car and, as they bent into the boot to reach the picnic basket, Merle's bare arm brushed against his. His heart raced; he felt as if he could not breathe; he felt the red hot blushes of his face as his blood pounded and Merle gave a sidelong look at him, then a low husky laugh. The smell of her perfume seemed to envelop him and he felt his legs trembling.

As they straightened up from the boot of the car, she looked straight into his eyes. She had the most beautiful blue/violet eyes with long eye lashes; a slow kind of secret smile appeared on her face.

'Come, let's get changed,' she said, as she lifted off her halter top and dropped her skirt on the sand. He felt his heart pounding as if it would burst; her beauty and perfection in the swimming costume she had already put on made him feel dizzy.

'Come in as soon as you're changed,' she said, as she raced down the beach into the sea. He stood awhile, wanting his heart to ease down. He did not understand what was happening to him. 'Hurry up,' she called out, 'the water is lovely.'

He got behind the car; he seemed all thumbs as he dropped his trousers and tore off his shirt. He put the swimming trunks on and, forgetting his fear of water, he ran down the beach, plunged into the warm sea, and started to swim towards her. She waited until he had caught up with her. She was smiling and called out 'Isn't this lovely.' Then she plunged under and came up so very close and he thought she was utterly beautiful. She pulled him closer and started laughingly to pull him under. Next moment their bodies were entwined and she kissed him. The shock was electric causing him to open his mouth and swallow the sea water which made him choke and splutter.

He broke to the surface, coughing and stammered and, for a moment, his fear of water took over, then he had it under control. Merle had also broke to the surface. 'Are you all right?' she asked, her voice and look full of concern. He nodded. 'Let's sit on the beach for a while,' Merle suggested, so they swam back, his brain reeling; she had kissed him, this beautiful goddess had actually kissed him. He did not know what was happening but his heart was singing and his body betraying him.

He grabbed a towel as soon as they left the water, hoping and praying that this wonderful angel would not notice the lump that he could not keep down. Somehow, they were laying on the sand together; she leaned over him, 'Are you all right, my darling?' she asked.

'Oh! yes, yes,' he replied. Oh! why could not his body behave.

She turned sideways. 'You have not had much experience with women, have you my darling?' she whispered, as she bent over his face, looking again with that deep searching look into his eyes.

'No,' he managed to mumble, his mouth so dry, as if he had a terrible thirst.

'Oh! my poor darling,' Merle whispered, 'Am I frightening you?'

'No, no, it's just so very wonderful. I have never been kissed by anyone, except my sister, before.'

'Oh! you poor darling,' she murmured and, bending over, kissed him again.

He felt he was going to faint as her lips brushed his, slowly and softly. 'Open your lips lightly, dear one,' she said, 'You only kiss relations with your lips together.'

He felt her arms go around him. Dazed, he opened his lips and felt her crush down more closely, then her tongue entered his mouth, probing and searching. He felt his arms go around her, crushing her to him. Her whole body was now on top of him: he was bewildered and dazed; his heart and blood pounding; Oh! this glorious, divine creature, he could feel every outline of her body.

She eased herself off him slightly and somehow moved his swimming costume down and her soft, smooth hand was holding his throbbing manhood, now so proud and firm. She ran her fingertips up and down as it throbbed. Huskily she whispered 'Wait, my darling,' moving back off him she released her own costume. Through the haze, he briefly beheld her marvellous body with her twin peaks jutting out proud and firm, then, somehow, he was on top of her and she slowly eased his manhood into what she called her jewel. His face encased in her beautiful breasts. Oh! the sheer joy, then nature took over and he was moving in rhythm with her. She whispered 'Come, Oh! come, my own darling.' He seemed to be floating, then her legs clamped around him as he soared and soared, then it poured out of him, draining him; it seemed to come down his very spine, as they moved violently up and down. Then, moaning his name over and over again, her legs unlocked and he fell to her side.

'Oh! my darling,' she said. 'That was wonderful. Am I really your first girl?'

'Oh! yes, Oh! yes,' he answered. 'I love you, I love you, Merle.'

As they lay in each others arms, looking into each others eyes, he still could not understand what had happened but thought how wonderful this goddess had returned his love.

Oh! how lucky he was.

153

Chapter Fourteen

He felt her hands move slowing over his body as her lips kissed his eyes, lips and throat; her fingers, searching and caressing his chest, moved down to his manhood, now laying weak and spent.

He copied her, moving his hand over her exquisite body, kissing every inch he could reach. She caught his hand and guided it to what, she whispered, was her jewel in the forest. Just feeling the silken soft hairs around her jewel sent thrills through his whole being.

Taking his hand inside, she whispered huskily 'Darling, find the spot that starts any woman.'

'I don't want anyone but you,' he cried. 'I love you, you're so beautiful.'

'Oh! dearest,' she said, 'you're so inexperienced, you will have others.'

'Never! Never! Gosh, you are so wonderful, so very beautiful, how could I want anyone but you?' They whispered to each other of the joy they had found then her hand moved back down his body and he felt it answering again; his blood pounding, his body alive to every caress, until he thought he must surely faint this time.

He heard her husky voice saying 'Darling, we shall do it slower this time.' When he was above her, she guided what she called his key into her jewel once again.

'Slowly, darling,' she murmured, 'slowly.' Their arms around each other, they kissed each others eyes, lips and throat as they slowly moved in rhythm. He had never known such exquisite pain and joy as their bodies moved in such unison. Then her legs clamped around him, holding him tight, as their rhythm moved faster and faster.

She started to moan and say the most exciting things. He was all man, she kept saying over and over again; her breath, like his, started to come in short bursts as they moved faster and faster; she heaved up and arched her back as her fingers raced up and down and tore into his skin. She screamed 'Take me, take me, darling,' as they crushed together.

He heard a voice saying, 'Oh! goddess, goddess, you're so lovely, so divine,' and realised it was his. Then he knew no more as their rhythm became a frenzy of movement.

He felt his strength drain away as he poured forth into her jewel and, as his rhythm slowed and the haze started to clear as he gulped for air, she gave a violent arch and screamed, then she went completely limp. They moved apart slowly, perspiration pouring out. 'Oh! darling,' she murmured, 'I have never had it as good as that. Are you sure I am the first?'

'Oh! yes, yes,' he replied.

'Well,' she said, 'it was terrific and I am so proud to be your first. You were really something.' He felt a glow of pride that he had made her so happy and satisfied, although he still could not understand how he could be so lucky as to have found such a beautiful angel and one that loved him in return.

After laying and relaxing in the warm sun and getting their breath back, Merle suggested a quick dip in the sea, then off to the summer cottage, half a mile down the coast, and have the picnic there. All the way down to the holiday cottage, still in their swimming trunks, with the car top thrown open and the hot sun drying them as they went along, he just sat sideways looking at her. He was trying to come to terms with what had happened at the cove, that this beautiful, marvellous goddess and he had made love; that she had held and kissed him and had murmured exciting things to him just as he had to her; that she felt like he did, she returned his love. How, just how, could he be this lucky?

Every now and then she would take her eyes off the narrow coast road to look at him with that secret, slow smile that made his heart flip.

'Stop looking at me all the time, darling,' she said in that husky exciting voice.

'I cannot help it,' he replied, 'you're so beautiful.'

She gave a deep chuckle and said 'Oh! Darling, you have so much to learn.'

On their arrival at the holiday cottage, which turned out to be a lovely wood built bungalow with a step at the front, the Zulu couple who looked after it, and cleaned and cooked for the 'Plains', rushed out to greet them. After the welcome, Merle introduced him as their guest and asked if they had received her message and got the guest room ready. On receiving an affirmative. Merle said to him 'Joseph will show you to your room, then come straight back for a shower. I am sure you're feeling hot and sticky.'

A real surprise awaited him. Laid out in the guest room on the bed were two pairs of trousers, one thin blue cotton, one a proper set of grey flannels, two short sleeved shirts, one blue, one white, and two sets of khaki shorts and shirts and, at the foot of the bed, two pairs of shoes and one pair of sandals.

After Joseph had left him, he sat on the bed and a flush of hot shame swept over him. Did he look that poor and scruffy that they had bought him clothes so that he would not be an embarrassment when they went out together.

After a while, Merle arrived at the door. Seeing his face, she came and sat next to him. 'What is it, darling,' she asked, as she put an arm around him. He started to blurt out that he had had enough charity in his life; that he knew his clothes were patchy and scruffy, but it was all he could afford right now.

'Oh! darling,' said Merle, her voice even huskier, 'that's not the reason I bought the clothes. It was because I love you and I know you don't get time off the ship during the day to go shopping so I guessed your measurements and went shopping for you.'

She turned towards him and pulled his head between her firm, satin twinned peaks. 'Come,' she said, 'let's shower, we're all alone. I have sent Joseph and his wife off to the village shopping and they won't be back for a couple of hours.'

As she stood up and pulled him towards her, he felt his body starting to betray him again. Merle gave a deep throated laugh. 'Oh! honey,' she said, 'let's shower,' giving a quick press and movement close to him as their arms crushed their bodies together.

Pulling away, she took his hand and led him to the small shower room. Quickly, she had her costume off and started to soap herself down. He had stood open mouthed at her sheer beauty; he had never seen a woman standing naked before. She looked, in his eyes, perfection.

'Come in, sweetheart, and join me.' Somehow, he got his shorts off and now they were soaping each other. Every now and then her hand would soap his manhood which was, by now, hard, firm and throbbing, while her peaks were just as firm and pointing. She guided his hand down and said 'Yes, oh! yes, darling.' Then, throwing the soap out, with the shower still running, she leaned back against the side and, with her hands around his buttocks she said, 'Take me, take me, darling, put that lovely key in my jewel.' As he entered her, she moved with him, their bodies as one, slipping and swaying. His heart pounding, he seemed to be floating.

If it had been good on the beach, this was fantastic. He dimly heard her scream and tell him he was wonderful as her body suddenly arched hard against him, and he felt the hot liquid pour forth inside her lovely jewel, as they both sagged and went limp together, their breath coming in short bursts.

'Darling,' she said, between panting breath, 'let's go and lie down for a moment.'

With that, she led him to her bedroom where they lay until both felt rested and his heart beat returned to normal. As they lay for awhile in each others arms, she said 'Darling, that was really something, thank you.'

He looked into her lovely violet/blue eyes and said 'Merle, darling Merle, it's I should be thanking you. Gosh! you're so very wonderful and I do love you so.'

She put one of her fingers over his mouth and said 'Hush, we shall have a long talk later.'

She sat up, saying 'Come, darling, I am hungry. Let's get the picnic basket out of the car and eat on the beach.'

As they sat eating, a few people walked by and waved. It appeared there were a few holiday cottages along this strip of beach. Like Merle's, they were rented and the Zulu couple came with the rent.

He ate, but never even knew what he was eating. Her nearness and beauty, her sweet smelling body, was all he could think about. He was finding it hard to absorb that he had actually held, kissed, caressed and entered this true goddess, this beautiful angel on earth.

They paddled in the sea, walked on the beach, laid on their towels and talked and all the time he longed to hold her, kiss her, but, as Merle pointed out, this was a very public beach and people knew her and David. The cove was fine because it had been empty.

So he spent the whole period, until darkness fell, just looking and worshipping her.

Darkness falls early in Africa and soon a slight breeze came off the sea. Merle gave a little shudder and, with a deep smouldering look into his eyes, said 'I think we will go back to the cottage and put something warm on and say good-bye to our swimming trunks until tomorrow.'

Once back at the Cottage out of the breeze, it was quite warm. He put a pair of his new shorts and shirt on and went and joined Merle in what was called the lounge or sitting room.

Merle said, 'Oh! Darling, they fit you perfectly. I am so glad I guessed the right size. Come, I will show you around the cottage.' Apart from the two bedrooms, there was the shower room, sitting room, kitchen and toilets and, at the back, three hundred yards away, was the hut that the Zulu couple lived in.

They went and sat out on the stoep in the dark and talked while Joseph and his wife prepared the dinner.

Merle asked him about his childhood in more detail, but mostly he talked about the 'Stophers' and his sister. He felt that to bring up all the ugly parts of his childhood would tarnish this wonderful period, but Merle still coaxed some of the hard parts out of him.

'Oh! you poor darling,' she exclaimed, reaching over to squeeze his hands. As he leaned forward to kiss, she pulled back, whispering, 'Not now darling. Don't forget Joseph and his wife.'

A thrill went through him. 'Did that mean he would be able to kiss and hold her later,' he whispered back.

He could just make out her delightful smile as she whispered back 'Of course, darling, later.'

Just as they sat down to dinner, the phone rang. As Merle answered it, she looked across at him as she said 'So you won't make it tonight, David.' His heart gave a lurch. It would appear it was David phoning to say he could not make it. In a daze, with his heart starting to race, he heard Merle telling David that they had a swim, a walk on the beach, then the picnic.

As Merle returned to the table, looking straight into his eyes, she said 'David cannot make tonight,' adding, 'poor you, darling, you will only have me for company.'

He blushed and stammered until she gave her husky laugh and said 'It's all right, darling, I think and feel the same and am glad we are having longer to ourselves.'

As the Zulu couple served the meal he was surprised to note how young Joseph's wife was. Nearly as tall as Joseph, she was a young, willowy sort of girl – she looked about twenty to Joseph's fifty – and she walked with a proud tilt of her head. It was obvious, as the meal progressed, the young Zulu girl thought a lot of Merle, fussing over her and making her eat.

The meal was first class. Once they had finished the dessert, Merle said they would have their coffee out on the stoep to give the couple a chance to clear away and wash up.

As they sipped their coffee, Merle said 'As soon as the couple have left to go to their home for the night, would you turn the two oil lamps, hanging from the roof of the stoep, off for me, darling. I always feel the light attracts the insects.'

Later, as they sat watching the moon shining on the sea and heard the hiss of the waves running up and down the beach, Joseph came to say goodnight and asked what time did they want a call. Merle told him 0700hrs would be early enough.

Once they had gone, he put out the lamps. As he turned from the second lamp, he found Merle had left her chair and was beside him. 'There, darling, is that not better,' she asked, as she put her arms around him pulling him close.

'Just think, my darling,' she said, 'we are now alone for the whole night.' He felt the thrill as he heard the words 'all night'.

'Do you mean I can sleep with you tonight?'

Merle gave a deep throated chuckle. 'I don't know about sleep, darling, but we will be together all night.'

Then they were in each others arms, kissing, caressing. Merle murmured 'Darling, let's go inside and enjoy each other.' Somehow, they were in her bedroom undressing each other and then on the bed. He was to remember that night forever; they ascended to great heights of indescribable sexual, exotic demands, leaving them both, in the early hours, utterly satiated, sapped of strength, yet floating after a taste of paradise, What Merle did not know about sex, and how to extract the most from any encounter, must have been nil.

As the dawn started to break, Merle whispered 'Darling, sailor boy, go and sleep in your own bed. We don't want Joseph finding us together.'

Exhausted as he was, he raised himself up, bent over to kiss her as he left the bed and thought Gosh, she still looks beautiful and desirable. Reaching his own bed, he fell onto it and was fast asleep in one minute.

Merle awoke him with a kiss. As he opened his eyes, he found her bending over him. 'Come on, lazy lump,' she said, her beautiful eyes twinkling. He sat up wide awake. Looking at her so alive, so vibrant, it was hard to believe this was the same goddess who had taught him so much last night and who, like him, had been utterly drained.

He stretched out his arms to hold her but, with that lovely heart slipping smile, she moved back whispering, 'Not here, darling, the servants. Come, shower and have breakfast then we can go to the beach.'

After he had had breakfast and Joseph had put a picnic basket in the boot, they got in the car and Merle, who seemed even more alive than before and was full of smiles and laughter, drove to the cove, only to find another couple already there.

'Never mind,' said Merle, giving him that secret half smile and leaning across to caress his manhood through his swimming shorts, 'there are plenty of coves along this strip of coast line.'

Sure enough, after two more false stops, they found an empty cove. Merle smiled at his impatience to take her in his arms.

'My, my,' she chuckled. 'Is this the shy young sailor of yesterday?' He found himself blushing and tried to say something but she put her finger to his mouth, saying 'I am only teasing you, my darling lover.'

Once out of the car, he took her into his arms and they kissed slowly, just brushing each others lips, before he explored inside her mouth with his tongue. Just as their bodies started to respond. Merle pulled away. Looking at him with smouldering, lovely eyes, she said, in the husky exciting voice, 'Darling, we have to talk first and I want you to listen very carefully as your response will dictate how we spend the next few precious hours we have left together. Darling sailor, you asked me twice last night when I was going to tell David that you and I had fallen in love. You also asked me when I was going to leave David for you. The answer to both questions, my darling, is never.'

As he started to speak, Merle quickly put her fingers on his mouth. 'Hush, dear sailor,' she said, 'let me finish.'

'First,' she continued, 'there is more than one way of loving. I have fallen in love with you but I also love my husband. A different kind of love, true, but a love based on years of living, loving and being together and mutual respect. Also, my love, although I hate to admit it, I am thirty years old to your fifteen years.'

'I don't care,' he shouted, 'I love you. You're so beautiful, I don't care about your age, I will never stop loving you.'

'Oh! you darling, if only that were true. You may think that now but, believe me, in one or two years, you will have been in love with others,' Merle said, in sad undertones.

'Never, never,' he replied.

Then, my darling sailor, let's look at another situation. If I did leave my husband, where would we live? How would you keep me? Look after me? You told me yourself you only get £2. 5s. 0d. a month. One has to be realistic in this world, darling. I don't want to hurt you, and I am not being mercenary, but you must admit your wage would not keep my car on the road let alone buy me a house, clothes and other things ladies like. Please say you understand, darling.'

His head was in a whirl, he felt betrayed, yet he knew in the clarity of his mind, she was right. Yet he loved her so. He looked up into her anxious looking face, her lovely eyes seemed to be pleading for him to understand. He nodded.

As Merle's lovely face lit up and her beautiful eyes looked into his with that special look that made his heart flip, he said 'But when I am older and climb up the ladder at sea, and earn a man's wage, I shall ask you again.'

'Oh! darling,' cried Merle, 'please do.'

Then they were in each others arms and they made love, crushing and aggressively, as if they were trying to blot out the previous half hour. At last, bruised and exhausted, their sweat mingling together, they lay panting in each other's arms.

'Thanks, darling,' Merle's husky voice whispered, and he knew she was really saying thanks for being so understanding rather than for the rough sex they had just had.

Now that Merle had explained everything, somehow they seemed even closer. Every time he looked at her, the sheer beauty of her still stunned him. Gosh! how he loved the closeness of her.

They opened the picnic basket and, as they ate the cold chicken and salads, Merle drank the Chablis while he drank the chilled lemonade, and they talked more freely than previously as if Merle's declaration about them, and her relationship with David, had somehow freed them. She did not want to hurt him or David and, when they arrived back to David's parish and home, she was relying on him not to let David guess what had happened between them.

'Do you love me enough not to let me down, darling,' she asked, 'or should I take you straight back to the ship and tell David that you had to go on duty?'

He looked into her beautiful eyes and said 'I promise never to tell anyone, ever, what has happened between us. David will never know from me.'

They had a swim in the sea and he made sure he never went out so far that he was unable to touch bottom with his feet, although Merle tried to coax him to swim out further.

Later, laying on their towels, Merle said, 'We shall have to go soon, darling. We have to pick up our bags and cases at the cottage then drive home. David will be expecting us for dinner tonight.'

They turned in towards each other, kissing gently, caressing tenderly. They made love slowly, deeply, and became one. Later, he often thought that that last lingering time they made love was in some way the best. Merle appeared as sad as him when, eventually, they got back into the car and left the cove. As they rejoined the road, Merle stopped the car. As they looked back down the cove, she leaned over, brushing his lips with hers, her husky voice saying 'We shall come back, darling, one day.'

'Oh! yes, oh! yes,' he had answered.

Picking up their bags and suitcases, saying goodbye to Joseph and his wife, they headed for David and home.

On arrival at the house, David came out to greet them. 'Sorry I could not join you. Had a good time?' he inquired. Merle assured him they had and how sorry they both were he had not made it.

'Dinner's just ready so, as soon as you have freshened up, we will eat,' David continued.

The meal was a painful time for him. He found it hard to look David in the face and was glad, when the meal was over, to sit around their outdoor swimming pool in dim lights.

After a while, David said he thought he would have an early night. 'Good idea, darling,' said Merle, 'I think we are all tired. An early night would do us all good.'

He had just got into bed, in a pair of lovely pyjamas David had lent him, when there was a knock at on the door and Merle called out 'Can I come in.'

His heart flipped over as he called out 'Yes.' As Merle entered, she threw her dressing gown wide open so that he could see her naked body underneath. Reaching the bed, she bent over and kissed him goodnight. A slow exciting kiss, while his hands reached up to touch her peaks. She gave a low chuckle and said 'Goodnight, my sailor,' pulled the dressing gown back around her and left.

On calling him in the morning, David informed him that they had received a phone call. Merle's Aunty Jane had been taken very ill. Merle had left early at 0600hrs for Port Elizabeth and he, David, would follow her after Evensong.

After a shower and late breakfast, David asked him if he wanted to use their swimming pool, explaining that a colleague was taking Morning Service so he was free until Evening Service. But he hardly heard anything David had said. The sudden departure of Merle had left him feeling dazed. He could not seem to accept the fact that she had gone.

'I never got the chance to say goodbye and thank her,' he managed to blurt out.

'Merle said to let you sleep and to tell you we will get in touch when your ship returns, and she will send the photo she promised you as soon as her favourite Aunty recovers,' replied David.

After moping around the pool feeling full of self pity, he asked David if he could go back to the ship now instead of after Evensong.

By the look of relief on David's face, it was obvious David had been waiting for just that suggestion.

Packing his case and bag, even with all his new clothes, did not take long and soon David was driving into the city and then the docks.

At the gangway, as he said goodbye and thanked David for

everything, he asked David how far away Port Elizabeth was.

'Oh! a few hundred miles up the Coast,' David replied.

As he turned to go up the gangway, David put his hand on his shoulder and surprised him by saying 'Women are funny creatures, don't be too hurt later.'

He carried on up the gangway, turned to wave, but David had already got in his car and was driving away. He wondered what David meant. Had he guessed something had happened between him and Merle?

By nightfall, he was already back into the ship's routine. His cabin mates, after giving him a welcome back and admiring his new clothes, left him onboard while they went ashore to paint the town red.

He went and made his report to the Chief who, apart from expressing surprise that he was back so early and asking where the couple had taken him over the weekend, was also just on his way ashore.

He lay in his bunk that night and relived every moment spent with Merle and thought how lucky he was to meet such an angel.

Two days later they sailed, but only to lay off the port for a whole week awaiting the formation of the convoy.

From where they lay at anchor off the coast, he could actually see the coast road along which Merle and he had travelled.

After a week at anchor off the port, during which time the number of ships at anchor had reached forty-eight, consisting of all different nationalities, the Navy signalled all ships to proceed to their allotted position in the formation of the next convoy for Aden. After a lot of chivvying and chasing, the Navy got the merchant ships in columns of three. At 1400hrs the Commodore signalled the convoy to proceed; next stop Aden.

He stood on deck watching South Africa fade from sight feeling heartsick; when would he see Merle again?

Travers came and stood by him and said 'Well, Titch, that's that.' He had replied 'I will never forget the past few days in that port.'

Travers answer surprised him. 'Oh! grow up Titch, you have been moping on deck, looking at the coast, ever since we left port.' He continued, using a crude expression seaman used the world over, 'If I did not know you better, I would say you were cock happy.' He had felt himself go red and turned away growling 'What would you know,' and went into the Engineer Officers' saloon.

That night, the Chief took to his bunk ill. He had been off colour and off his food for a few days but had refused a Doctor. Ship owner's did not like medical bills in those days and, for a senior officer to cause the shipping company any expense, could cost him his job on arrival back in the U.K.

As the days passed, the Chief got progressively worse and his temperature reach 103°. With the weather getting hotter by the hour and no wind no matter which way one put the weather shutes in the portholes, the Captain at last decided to signal the destroyer escort and ask their Doctor for advice.

Meanwhile, he had been allowed into the Chief's cabin and he and Abdul took turns wiping him down, as the perspiration poured forth and the Chief's skin turned a putty grey. After the Navy Doctor had received all information regarding pulse, temperature, etc., the destroyer came alongside and, on the loud hailer, amid laughter from its crew, suggested the Chief needed a warm soap water enema by way of the anus.

Even the Captain had to smile as he acknowledged the message and thanked the Navy for its help.

So, with great fanfare and laughter, the Captain and Chief Steward gave the Chief a warm soap water injection up the anus, with half the crew shouting advice through the portholes. It certainly worked and the Chief was up and eating in two days, but it took him a lot longer to live down the wisecracks and jokes.

On arrival at Aden, the ship bunkered. There was coal dust everywhere, in your bunk, food, water. As you breathed in, one breathed coal dust and the heat did not help—tempers became very frayed.

But it was brought home to him very forcefully that his childhood had not been that bad compared with the young children in Aden where boys between the age of ten to fifteen, and young girls between the age of fifteen and twenty, were bunkering the ship and carrying onboard, in bags, the coal the ship needed. Line after line of them came up one large wide ladder carrying the coal on their backs, tipped the coal into the bunker, then went down the second ladder to pick up another bag of coal. They were a human conveyor belt. It took two nights and a day, using hundreds of these children to load the hundred of tons required for the ship.

Leaving Aden, the old *Llandudno* joined another convoy bound for Port Said then Alexandria.

The heat was so great in the Red Sea that the cook had to boil a lot of barley for the poor firemen to drink. It seems that barley water was thought to help stop the terrible dehydration the firemen were suffering, but things got worse. There were so many firemen laid up with heat exhaustion that the Captain asked for volunteers from the deck crew and catering to help below.

Travers and himself had gone to help but the terrific heat in the stoke hold had soon driven them out. Besides which, he found that after plunging the slice (big iron bar) into the fire as Abdul taught him, he had neither the weight nor strength to move the large clinkers, pull as he might. Being on deck actually felt cool after the experience but, for about three days, the engine room could not raise enough steam and the ship had to fall away from the convoy. The most the ship could do was about six knots.

As things got better and the firemen recovered, the old lady got back to the great speed of nine knots, but with no hope of catching the convoy.

Eventually, they arrived off Port Tawfig at the Suez Canal, Egypt, and caught up with their convoy who were waiting to proceed up the Canal. It was all new and very exciting. In the morning, they entered the Canal; he stood on deck and marvelled as the desert slipped by on each side of the ship. He even saw a detachment of the famous Camel Corps charging past, the camels going at great speed. Not even the heat, flies, smells or bumboats could take away his thrill on his first time in the Suez Canal.

Stripey, in charge of the D.E.M.S. Gunners, explained how, before the Canal was built, at the Port Tawfig end there used to be tides every twenty-four hours, and that Moses had taken his people across while the tide was out and the Egyptian Army was caught with its pants down when the tide came in. With the Canal being cut through, the tides, of course, disappeared. As the story did not gel with what he had been taught, he took Stripey's version with a grain of salt. Years

166

later, an Egyptian historian assured him it was quite true—another myth exposed.

They spent the night in the Bitter Lakes, then proceeded to Port Said. Two nights later, with only three other ships but with five destroyers, they sailed for the Port of Alexandria. They arrived while an air raid was in progress. All on the ship had a grandstand view while the five destroyers all opened fire at the low flying German and Italian aircraft.

Going alongside, the dockers soon had the deck cargo ashore, the large boxes of aircraft badly needed at the front. With the corn beef having been taken off in South Africa and sent up by rail, the rest of the cargo consisted of tanks, ammunition and, surprise, surprise, large bags full of ladies' underwear and Tampax for the A.T.S.; this part of the cargo caused a lot of lewd remarks from the crew.

First night ashore in Alexandria, he visited the famous 'Mohammed Ali Square' where the night life was enlivened by a street fight between Free French and Vichy French sailors which the MPs had to break up. It appeared that this was a regular occurrence as there was a lot of bitterness between the two sides, especially as the Vichy French sailors were living on two large battle cruisers which they would not let the Free French use to fight the Germans, preferring to live on them in port and withdraw from the war.

Next morning, just after giving the Engineer Officers their coffee, one of the crew came in and informed him that an A.T.S. person was asking for him at the gangway.

As he rushed to the gangway, all the Engineer Officers also rushed to the shipside to look. On reaching the gangway, he saw his sister talking to the Dock Master.

Calling out her name, he rushed down and, next minute, was giving her a big hug and a kiss.

To him she still looked beautiful and, by this time, the crew and officers were all at the ship's side giving shouts and wolf whistles. He felt ten feet tall and so proud of his sister. He introduced his sister to the Chief and the other Engineer Officers. Although they were in their filthy oily overalls, they made a great fuss of her but he could tell his sister was not amused.

Ian, the apprentice deck officer, arrived with a message. The

Captain wanted to see them both at once on the Bridge.

When they arrived on the Bridge, it was obvious to him that the Captain had cleaned himself up and was, for once, now in immaculate whites, with his epaulettes of four thick gold bars gleaming on his shoulders. His sister had, on reaching the Bridge, stood stiffly to attention and saluted. The Captain had, with eyes twinkling, saluted back and then said. 'No need to salute me, this is a merchant ship.' His sister had replied 'I saluted out of courtesy, Captain, for allowing me onboard, and on your Bridge, to see my brother.' The Captain said he felt the Bridgehouse the most comfortable place for them both to talk, away from everyone. As he left them, the Captain said ,'Take as long as you like, boyo, I will clear it with the Chief about their dinner.'

As soon as the Captain left them he said, 'Oh! it's so wonderful to see you sis.'

'Well,' she answered, 'first things first. What on earth are you doing on this rusty old tramp? Last time I saw you, you were in bellbottoms and tunic. Look at you now, in dirty shirt and shorts and sandals with broken straps. What happened? When I got your letter from Cardiff that you had joined *S.S. Llandudno*, I thought you must be signals or something. What happened?'

He felt a little hurt at his sister's description of the ship that he had grown to love but he could see it from her point of view. It might look old and rusty but she would not appreciate the great feeling of comradeship the ship had.

So he told her about Yearly, what had happened; the placard he had made him wear while he marched up and down the parade ground. Even after all, these months, he started to choke up and his lips quivered as he relived his humiliation of that terrible day and he felt hot tears starting.

He felt his sister's arms go around him. 'Dearest little brother,' he heard her say, 'don't get upset, please. When I return to the U.K., I will go and sort him out.'

'Not if I get back to the U.K. first,' he had replied. Then his sister asked him, 'What did the Captain, or that nice Chief Officer at the Naval School, do about Yearly's treatment of you?'

'Nothing. For some reason they seemed frightened of him. They let him get away with murder.'

'Well,' she said, 'I will visit that Navy School, and the Homes H.Q., when I am back in the U.K.'

They talked for a long time, then his sister asked if he could get off the ship and come ashore.

He went off the Bridgehouse to the Captain's quarters, thanked the Captain for his kindness, and took his sister to the Chief and explained his sister would like to take him ashore.

'Go and enjoy yourself, boyo,' said the Chief, 'We can look after ourselves.' While he went to get changed, the Chief and Popeye entertained his sister.

Before leaving the ship, he took his sister to the galley to meet the cook and galley boy, then to the cabin he shared and introduced her to Travers and McSally, who he was surprised to see had really cleaned up their quarters, even made up his bunk. His sister was not impressed just the same. 'Do you mean three of you sleep in this small cabin? It cannot be more than ten feet by four feet.' He had replied an affirmative.

Taking his sister aft, he introduced her to the deck crew. There he got a surprise; they had cleaned themselves up and, for the first time since leaving Cardiff, Di Evans and Tudor Price had put their false teeth back in. He considered that a great compliment to his sister.

After leaving the deck and firemen's quarters, they made their way to the D.E.M.S. quarters. Here, for the first time since she had come onboard, his sister relaxed. The D.E.M.S. Gunners and Stripey, in their white shirts and shorts and Stripey's Petty Officer badges, was something she could cope with.

Sitting down amongst them, she told them, 'The last time I saw my brother, he was in bellbottoms and tunic. I have to say P.O. that I am surprised to see him like this.'

'Yes,' answered the P.O., 'and when you know how fast he is with morse and semaphore, it's doubly hard. Why he even gives deck apprentices and the third mate lessons, yet he signed on this ship as a pisspot jerker. Begging your pardon, young lady, but I feel it's such a waste.'

'So do I,' said my sister.

'But it was the only way I could get to sea,' he assured his sister.

They went ashore. On reaching the dock gates and showing their passes, the Sergeant of the Security Guard and Military Police, told his sister that an Army lorry was going to town and would give us a lift which would save paying for a gharry ride. So, for a few minutes, he watched how his beautiful sister handled the lecherous Sergeant, who obviously thought he was God's gift to women. Every pass or hint he made, she handled with a demure smile and flapping of her eyelids, till the poor man was flustered and completely off balance. In fact, he appeared relived to see the lorry come.

Climbing into the back of the lorry, waving to the Sergeant, once out of sight they had both exploded in laughter. On arriving up town, they found a cafe and his sister treated him to a meal and they talked and talked.

His sister had it all planned; they would live together after the war.

When he pointed out that she might be married and her husband might have something to say, she replied, 'If he does not agree to your living with me, no marriage.'

It was obvious, as the afternoon wore on, that his sister could not reconcile herself to the fact he was serving on such a dirty rusty ship. In vain, he tried to convey the great rapport and comradeship the whole ship had, and how he had come to love the ship. Tired engine, no showers or bathrooms, clanging chains, thick rust, cockroaches and rats, notwithstanding, to him she was a wonderful, happy ship.

He did not know, that afternoon, that in his whole thirty-five years at sea, he was never to know such happiness again on any ship, not even the most modern, newly built ship, would ever have a place in his heart that the old *S. S. Llandudno* had captured.

But, before the day was out, his sister had extracted a promise that he would leave the Merchant Navy and join the Royal Navy as soon as he reached the age of seventeen years.

They went to the A.T.S. Army Depot where his sister was billeted. After a chat with the guard, he was let in and his sister took him to the hut she shared with nine others, who promptly made a great fuss of him.

It would seem they had all been sent to pick up Army lorries that had landed at the docks then drive them to some depot in the desert.

After the other girls had left, his sister took him outside the hut and they carried on talking. Eventually, his sister got around to his having to be careful not to go with loose women, not to get V.D. or any other disease and not, under any circumstances, to go to the famous or infamous 'Sister Street' whilst in Alexandria.

'Oh! the lads went there last night,' he told his sister, who gave a sniff and said, 'That is no surprise, but you make sure you don't go.'

'No chance of me going,' he replied, 'because I am in love with Merle and I am saving myself for her, and only her.'

His sister had smiled at his young, emphatic statement. 'And who,' she asked, 'is Merle? Where did you meet her?'

'She is a wonderful girl I met in South Africa and when I have climbed up the ladder and earned a man's salary, she will leave her husband and marry me.' There was complete silence for a moment but he saw the smile had left his sister's face.

'Please explain what you mean, little brother. Who Is Merle? What do you mean she will leave her husband? How old is she, for God's sake?'

So he explained everything, from the moment the Captain had introduced the three boy ratings to the Reverend and Mrs. Plain, to the pain of parting. 'We never meant to fall in love, sis,' he finished, 'it just happened. She is so wonderful, you will love her.'

In the ensuing silence, he could see his sister was trying to control herself, then, 'What did you say the age of this woman was?' his sister's voice was angry and cold.

'Thirty years,' he replied, 'but age makes not a scrap of difference. She is so young looking and, anyway, we are in love.'

His sister's voice was so harsh and full of scorn. 'Love! the bitch seduced you. You have no experience about women, little brother, she just had her way with you. She took you as a virgin in these matters and seduced you. In fact, I would call it rape only in reverse, a female raping a young boy, and a parson's wife at that.' His sister's voice was raised in disgust and scorn. He, in return, was angry and deeply hurt by what his sister was saying.

He begged her not to speak like that about the only woman he had ever loved besides her, but his sister could not keep her contempt and anger for Merle under control. 'The bitch, the scheming bitch, poor innocent you, little brother.' In vain, he tried to explain, but his sister was adamant.

In his anguished cry from the heart that 'it was not like that', his sister realised that he really thought it was a genuine 'Love'. She wondered how she was going to convince him otherwise when two of the A.T.S. girls returned.

His sister called them over. Knowing how he was suffering inside at not only the first quarrel he had ever had with his sister, and that it should be over the first woman he had ever fallen in love with had made him heart sick, his sister decided desperate measures were called for.

As her two friends joined them, his sister said, 'Little brother, you think I am being hard and unjust, when it's because I love you that I said what I did. Please tell my friends exactly what you have told me and, if they don't agree with me, I will sincerely apologise. But, if they do agree, you must promise to hear me out without us having a quarrel, agreed?' He nodded, still in shock, at his beloved sister's attack on Merle.

So, for the second time that day, he told his story. When he had finished, one of the A.T.S. women said, 'You poor lad, the bitch should be put away'; while the other said 'That was a first class seduction, if not rape, I have ever heard of, and you say she was a parson's wife?' He nodded miserably. 'Well, all I can say, she sounds as though she has had a lot of practice in seducing young boys. Now you listen to your sister and she will guide you straight, like we all do when we want a shoulder to cry on.' With that, they left.

His sister put her arm around his shoulder and said, 'Have you had a letter from this Merle?'

'Not yet,' he mumbled.

'How many have you sent her?'

'Two via the pilot boat whilst at anchor off South Africa, two at Aden, two at Port Said.'

'Don't you think it funny,' asked his sister, 'no reply from six letters?'

'I put it down to wartime post,' he had answered.

'You could accept that if it were mail from the U.K., but not from South Africa. There are still civilian passenger aircraft from South Africa to Egypt three times a week, they bring the mail. I don't want to hurt you any more than you are, little brother, but I will be very surprised if you ever hear from that woman again and you certainly won't after I write to her,' his sister continued.

Still hurt and bewildered, he said, 'You don't know her address and I won't give it to you. You don't understand how I feel. I love her and am hurt that you, the sister I admire so much, should think the worst of Merle.'

'Well, you have to admit, my two friends felt exactly the same and it is only because I care so, that I am angry with your Merle. For God's sake, little brother, if she admits to being thirty, you can bet she's at least thirty five years old. You're only fifteen years old and, what's more, straight out of the orphanage, with no experience of women, except the 'Gussies' (Matrons) and you could hardly call them examples of passionate love.' He just had to giggle at the thought.

'That's better,' said his sister, 'I don't like you being unhappy.' They gave each other a big hug and talked, the anger gone. They decided to wait and see if he did hear from Merle and that his sister would not write any letters to her.

'Now, with that out of the way, let's go to the Fleet Club.' On the way to the club, he managed to extract a promise from his sister that she would not mention Merle to the Captain or anyone onboard.

The Fleet Club was a wonderful oasis for Service and Merchant Navy personnel in Alexandria. For those whose minds were above their navels and wanted a taste of 'home', the Fleet Club was a must, with its 'Housey-Housey' (later called Bingo), lovely cooked food, film shows and dancing.

Their arrival soon attracted the Romeos but his sister handled them, nicely but firmly, assuring them she would dance later but, right now, she and her little brother had a lot of talking and swapping yarns to do, as they had not seen each other for a long time. Funny enough, even the Romeos could identify with that and left.

After a meal, they moved to the Housey-Housey section, talking all the time. Later, his sister had danced but only once with any partner, and made sure no one joined their small table.

As he could not dance, he sat back and enjoyed watching the dancers. As he supped his lemonade, his thoughts turned to Merle. Although he had not told his sister, he was, in truth, finding it harder each day to capture the feeling of love, although she had not faded from his thoughts.

At the end of the night, his sister dropped him off at the dock gates on her way to her billet.

Next morning, she arrived onboard with Army overalls, shirts, shorts and shoes, and one of her friends, who was soon being entertained by the Chief and the other Engineer Officers, plus Popeye, whilst he and his sister had the use of the Bridgehouse again.

His sister explained that she could not stop long as they were due out with their new lorries at 1400hrs so, after two hours, she kissed him goodbye, reminded him of his promise to join the Royal Navy, and to keep clear of loose women. Also, she added with a smile, parson's wives.

As his sister left the ship with her friend, he and most of the ship's company, waved goodbye. He wondered when he would see her again.

The Chief must have guessed his thoughts. 'Don't you worry now, boyo,' he said, 'we will be back soon.'

No one dreamt then what we would all see before we were back in Alexandria. He certainly never knew that he would grow up inside a week, never to be youthful and relaxed ever again.

It started that very afternoon. Orders came for extra Army dockers to descend on the ship and get the remaining cargo out fast and they certainly did that. By midnight, the *S.S. Llandudno* was empty. The tugs towed her to the coaling depot where she was topped up in coal bunkers. At 0500hrs she was cleared for sea.

The Captain swore to the Chief that he did not know what was happening. All he knew was that the Navy had commandeered the ship and all shore leave was cancelled. Those ashore were soon picked up by the Navy shore patrol and returned to the ship and the Captain had orders, signed by the Admiral, that the *S.S. Llandudno*, loaded or unloaded, had to be cleared for sea and outside the breakwater by 0600hrs—and she was.

Once outside the port, the *S.S. Llandudno* joined five other merchant ships with five destroyers back on duty. The Navy got the merchant men into columns of two and they proceeded up the coast. Clear of port, the Navy signalled to the merchants ships that they were proceeding to Tobruk but to lay off Bardia first. Once the ship had settled into position, the Captain informed all hands where the ship was heading. He concluded, 'We all know from the radio that Tobruk is under attack and in a bad position. From the looks of the other ships with us, we have all been selected for our shallow draft. It's my guess Tobruk is going to have its own 'Dunkirk'. Everyone must keep their eyes peeled for aircraft and U-boats.'

It turned out the Captain was not far wrong. That afternoon, they had a taste of things to come. Around 0200hrs, they were attacked by Italian and German aircraft. For two hours they were under a sustained attack from torpedo planes and bombers, with fighter planes strafing the convoy from both sides, coming in again and again, from the sun; as soon as one attack finished, another started. Reality of war had at last come to him and he discovered he was so scared. He looked at the others in the first-aid team, they did not seem worried. In fact, Travers and the Chief Steward were cracking jokes. He knew he must not show how frightened he was—he would never live it down if he did.

Off Bardia, three large deep-sea tugs, towing barges, joined them. The tugs were nearly as big as the *S.S. Llandudno*. Just as they joined, one of the merchant ships was hit. Being light with no cargo, she remained afloat. The Navy ordered her Captain to beach her and get his crew ashore.

About ten miles from Tobruk, the Navy stopped the convoy opposite a large stretch of beach. Here the tugs, with their barges, raced for the beach and started taking the wounded off. Two miles further out at sea, there now appeared two large hospital ships, painted all white, with Red Cross markings on their sides. Someone said they were, in peacetime, passenger ships of the Union Castle Line.

Be that as it may, the Navy ordered the five remaining merchant ships, with their shallow draft, to ease closer and closer to the land to meet the tugs, which were now bringing off the badly wounded.

At fifteen, he at last learnt the true horror of war, steaming back and forth, over and over again, taking the gallant wounded to the hospital ships and, at the same time, under aircraft attacks. The destroyers put up a terrific barrage to cover them. One destroyer was hit. They were so near they could see the flames breaking out all over, then, with a roar, she was gone. The blast was so fierce that it nearly turned a tug over—it certainly washed all the wounded on her barge overboard; there was no time to stop and pick them up.

The wounded had been bandaged and strapped up somewhere ashore but all the movement had loosened some bandages, plus a lot of the wounds opened up. There was blood everywhere, on the barge, on the *Llandudno* decks, but the most obscene of all was to see the blood dripping from the cargo nets as they were swung onboard the hospital ships. He vomited, then fainted, but the Chief Steward slapped his face and he had pulled himself together. Half of the wounded seemed to be, from their shoulder flashes, the 2nd South African Division, the rest an assortment of 32nd Tank Brigade, 51st Division and Guards Brigade.

He saw men without arms, legs and some blind, and felt their pain and suffering in the heat and flies.

Barge load after barge load of soldiers, destroyed in body and some in mind, were brought off from the beach. The destroyers were doing a marvellous job of keeping the German and Italian aircraft at bay, as they circled around the merchant ship. Every now and then, the hard pressed shore batteries also put up a barrage of fire power to assist hard pressed destroyers.

On the second morning, after a fitful night of U-boat alerts, the electric power on *S.S. Llandudno* failed. It was the old voltage of 110 volts. The Captain informed the Navy that they could not maintain signals by lamping. A destroyer asked how long before power could be restored as it was imperative that contact was maintained between all ships. After the Captain's reply on the hailer that they were doing their best to trace the fault, the Navy decided to put a signaller onboard to use flags and semaphore. The Captain informed the destroyer that he already had a first class signaller, Navy trained, who would do all semaphore signalling until power was restored.

The Captain sent for him and said,

'Now, boyo, up on the monkey isle with those flags and, after you read their messages, inform me and I will tell you what reply to send but, in an air attack, come into the Bridge. Now, you understand, bach?'

'Yes, Captain,' he replied and shot up to the monkey isle. The Chief Radio Operator was already there. 'Hello, Titch,' he said, 'Sorry about this but they only taught us radio and Morse. I'm hopeless on flags.'

For nearly two hours he semaphored, his arms started to ache, when the Chief informed the Captain, power was restored.

He returned to his duties of giving the soldiers drinks of water and trying to keep the canvas covers over their poor bodies. In the meantime, the D.E.M.S. Gunners got their first kill, an Italian aircraft, which had got through the barrage of gunfire. The D.E.M.S. were cock-a-hoop.

By evening on the second day, the two hospital ships had reached saturation point and could receive no more human cargo. They departed for Alexandria at full speed. It was to the German and Italian airmen's credit that not once did they attack or go near the hospital ships.

The Navy ordered the merchant ships to take onboard as many of the wounded as possible. There were wounded laying everywhere on the old *S. S. Llandudno* when the signal came to form up for the race back to Alexandria which, apart from one U-boat alert, was achieved in peace.

The berth in Alexandria was astern of the hospital ships and they could see the wounded were still being unloaded from them.

The Army and Airforce medical teams poured onboard, taking their human cargo ashore, some already dead.

Around 2000hrs the whole dockside seemed to go silent as a piper from one of the ships started to play the Scot lament 'Flowers of the Forest'. The clear tone of the bagpipes filled the air. It was a funny sensation standing on the deck, hearing the tune; the back of his head tingled as his hair stood out. It was a lovely moving experience and, for some reason, he started to cry, although he did not realise he was until he felt the tears running down his face.

Someone in the crew said it was a piper from one of the Clan Line Ships.

Next morning, one of the crew caused a sensation. He claimed he had just seen some German P.O.W.s in the cage at the top of the dock and that some of them had a shamrock on their sleeves, Irish men fighting for the Germans. Some of them went to have a look and returned to confirm the story.

He had asked the Chief, 'How could they fight for Germans?'

The Chief said, 'They also re-fuel U-boats, their fishing boats inform the German Consuls every time they see a British Convoy so if some of them are actually fighting, this should not surprise you, bach.'

But Stripey said he was very surprised. 'After all,' he said, 'putting bombs in letter boxes, and other places, to hurt innocent unarmed civilians, or shooting someone in the back, is more the I.R.A. style—they don't usually fight face to face.'

He had felt so ashamed that he had been born in Ireland.

Next day, they received orders to proceed to Massawa, Italian Somaliland, which had been captured by British and Australian troops, via Port Said, Suez Canal and the Red Sea.

Before leaving, he received two letters, one from South Africa. On opening it, he found it was from David informing him that they were moving to a new parish near Port Elizabeth and would he please not write any more as he and Merle found his letters unwelcome.

The second letter was from a cook in one of the Homes, who wrote to say they prayed for his safety every day and he would be welcome to stay at their house any time he came on leave. It appeared she had left the Homes, married a nice local chap, and they both assured him of a warm welcome.

He tore up David's letter and put the other in his locker.

As they entered the Canal, news came through that Tobruk had fallen; it was 17th June.

Years later, he heard armchair critics on the television complaining there were no neuro-surgeons at the Falklands War and that some of the troops, who had not even reached the battle zone, had to receive counselling. His thoughts returned to that period of his life, when there had not been a first aid orderly let alone a Doctor onboard, and certainly no busybody counsellors to counsel anyone. But they had all suffered and he had not heard one complaint pass any soldiers' lips. What had happened between the 1940s and 1980s?

They had taken on more livestock at Alexandria so they were sure of fresh meat—the condi crystals were not used for this part of the voyage.

Once in the Red Sea, the heat returned but somehow, after

Alexandria and Tobruk there was just an acceptance, not a lot of moaning and groaning.

At last they arrived at Massawa and entered the large floating dry-dock. It was a magnificent feat of engineering. The *S.S. Llandudno* was dwarfed by the floating dock, which was still manned by the Italians but, of course, overseen by the British Army. He was intrigued to meet and even talk to some of the Italian engineers, they seemed so harmless and it was hard to think of them as the enemy.

The heat in Massawa was terrible, far worse than out in the Red Sea, perspiration just poured out of everyone day and night.

After three days and nights of scraping, painting and engine room repairs, the ship left Massawa for Aden. After replenishing stores, they joined a convoy for South Africa. With her bottom scrapped of all the barnacles, the dear old *S.S. Llandudno* could sometimes even reach 10 knots.

On arrival at Capetown, everyone onboard relaxed, seeing the bright lights, shops full of everything, no blackout, and the people going about their business, and kind, wonderful people still streaming down to the docks to take the lads out.

For a night, it was hard to believe that this country had just lost the cream of its youth in North Africa; that there were thousands of parents in South Africa who would never see their sons again, their only comfort—that their sons had made the supreme sacrifice against the Nazi hordes, helping to make the world a better place to live in.

Unfortunately for South Africa, peoples' memories all over the world were to be very short and their sacrifice soon forgotten.

After a week in Capetown, they left in a convoy for Freetown, Sierra Leone, with some ships, including the *Llandudno* to branch off for Takoradi, West Africa.

The trip was uneventful and, on leaving the convoy with six others, the old lady heaved a sigh of relief as her engines stopped and the anchor plunged down to bring the ship to rest off the Port of Takoradi.

The barges were soon alongside and the hatches open to receive bauxite, iron ore and copper. Once loaded, the ship left Takoradi in a small convoy to join a larger one at Freemantle.

On the first night out, war was brought home to them with a bang.

After Tobruk, the *Llandudno* had not seen any action, U-boats, raiders or aircraft, and had become relaxed but now the fear was back. The ship on the *Llandudno's* port side was hit; being loaded with ore and copper, she just sunk like a stone, so fast that her engine was still going as she went under in less than a minute. It was frightening to see a ship just disappear. The Navy dropped depth charges and chivvied their charges to squeeze another 2 knots out of their engines. When the ship at the stern of the convoy was hit, she, seemed to disappear even faster. How everyone cursed the bright moon, as the alarm bells rang again for action stations.

He had realised that night that he was not cut out to be a hero, he was truly scared but made damn sure he never showed it.

On reaching Freetown, they found the U.K. bound convoy waiting for them. Oh! the joy at the thought—U.K. bound—the crew even started to smile and forget the past nights.

After joining their allotted position, every ship in the forty strong convoy received a message from the Commodore's ship to watch their smoke, keep in station, and to watch out for U-boats, plus to make sure they kept a strict blackout at all times.

On the second night out, the U-boats struck. Two ships were lost and everyone was straining their eyeballs for torpedo streaks.

A week later, to keep them on their toes, the U-boats returned but, this time, only one ship was lost.

After three more weeks of storms and zigzagging, the convoy split up, some bound for Liverpool, but the grand old lady, with some of the other ships, was ordered to Cardiff. The atmosphere onboard was sheer joy and happiness, the officers and crew alike were in the throes of what seafarers call the 'channels', it affects every ship as they return home. Standing on deck entering Cardiff, he felt so proud of the *S.S. Llandudno*, even with the aft gun still pointing its barrel forlornly up in the air and its broken casing now thick with salt water rust but, like the day they sailed, hardly anyone even looked up from the dockside to look at the rusty old tramp returning from an eleven month voyage.

That night, before they all went ashore to celebrate, the Chief Engineer thanked him and gave him a glowing letter of recommendation in front of all the other Engineer Officers. 'He was,' the Chief assured him, 'the best mess boy I have ever had, boyo.' He felt ten feet tall.

Travers offered to take him home but he said he was going to visit the Home. The House Master and staff made him very welcome. The House Master also told him about the new rules in the Merchant Navy. You had to get your job through what was called the 'Pool' and no one was allowed to find their own jobs anymore; no Captains allowed to pick their own crews anymore, they had to take what the 'Pool' sent them. 'So, O'Dell,' the Master said, 'you were one of the last to look for his own berth.'

Just before he left, with the rest of the staff having gone about their duties, he told the Master about Tobruk and his awful nightmares, about seeing his sister, and how scared he had been off Takoradi, West Africa.

The Master said, 'Well, O'Dell, if you had not been frightened, that would have been a surprise. I know, from the last war, everyone is frightened in action and I am glad you saw your sister. As far as Tobruk is concerned, you will find, as I did, the nightmares will fade in time.'

As he left to return to the ship, the Master said, 'Oh! by the way O'Dell, don't go to the Naval School during your leave, they won't let you in.'

Next morning, everyone washed and in their best clothes, the, Captain announced the ship would pay off at 1100hrs. He stood on deck feeling sad, in a way, that he was leaving the old lady. Stroking her side, he told Travers he was going to miss the ship. Travers, who could not get off her fast enough, thought he was mad. 'This,' said Travers, 'is my first and last voyage in the Merchant Navy. Paying off cannot come fast enough for me.' McSally found them and told him the Captain wanted to see him pronto in the deck saloon. He arrived there in time to see the Chief Steward and the Captain showing the company representative the medical log for the voyage. Apart from the Chief Engineer Officer's bout of constipation, not one illness had been reported all through the eleven months of heat, storms, flies, cockroaches, rats and food that left a lot to be desired, not one member of the crew had fallen ill or reported sick.

The Captain looked up, saw him, and called, 'Come in, boyo.' As he approached, the Captain said to another man sitting at the saloon table, 'This is the young boy.' The man, who turned out to be from the shipping office, smiled at him and said, 'The Captain has been speaking very highly of you'—he felt himself go beetroot red—'especially your fast morse and how you semaphored from the monkey isle off Tobruk.'

Seeing him now red and perspiring, the shipping master said, 'Don't be embarrassed, son, it's just I wanted to inform you that there is a new system just come out called T124X. Roughly, it means that you serve on Royal Navy Ships and come under Royal Navy discipline but you are paid Merchant Navy salary and, of course, wear Royal Navy uniform. Are you interested?'

'Oh! yes Sir,' he had answered. The Captain laughed, 'I knew you would, boyo.'

He had filled in the forms there and then and would have reported then, but the Captain and Shipping Master both smilingly assured him he must have at least a two/three week rest from the voyage.

He rushed out to tell Travers, Chief and Stripey what he had done. They were all so happy for him. After he had paid off, he found, to his surprise, that nearly all the lads had decided to see him off at Cardiff Station. Saying goodbye to the Chief, the lads had carried him down the gangway into a waiting taxi, then followed by at least three other taxis, they went through the dock gates and on to the station for the Newcastle-on-Tyne train. Then, getting him a seat, they stood on the platform, waving and shouting, as the train pulled out jerking and banging its couplings.

He awoke with a start. Still half asleep, it took him a few moments to realise he had been daydreaming again. He was on a train all right but one that had just stopped abruptly at Cheltenham, not just leaving Cardiff. I must be getting old, he muttered to himself, that's the second time today I have dreamed of the past. Taking his case down from the rack, he left the train. Still, he thought, wait until Betty sees the Russia Medal. With a sigh of happiness, he shook the last cobwebs from his mind and headed for home.

A week later, the phone rang at their home. It was a local girl reporter and she asked if she could come and visit them. 'I have already been interviewed by your paper about the Russia Medal and the voyage to Russia,' he informed her.

'Yes, I know, but some of our readers have phoned to ask what happened when you left the hospital and, in any case, I would so like to meet you and your good lady.' It was arranged the reporter would call the next day at 1400hrs.

When she arrived, she turned out to be a charming young lady. After the three of them had settled in the lounge, drinking tea and eating homemade cake, he suggested that she should go ahead and ask any question she thought would interest anyone.

'Well, what I and the readers would really like to know is did you go to sea again during the war? Could you perhaps tell us what happened to you, from your arrival at the Military Ward till the end of the war?'

'Well, my stay at the hospital was both painful and, at times, enjoyable. The painful part was all the workouts on the parallel bars and a lot of therapy treatment in a small ward that had been converted to a gym, or a workout room. At the same time it had to be balanced against making sure the wounds between my legs and on my thighs did not break open. My legs, thank goodness, made a marvellous recovery, but the internal injuries took longer.

While at the hospital, the ex-cook from the Homes visited me with her husband. Soon as she saw me, grey-haired, toothless, and my legs under a basket type cover, she burst into tears, 'Oh! what have they done to you, you poor boy, and why are you wearing those blue tinted glasses.' After her husband and I had calmed her down, I explained that I was at least lucky to be alive, that I could soon dye my hair and had already been visited by the Army Dentist and would soon be receiving false teeth, but the poor dear took a lot of convincing. A nurse kindly brought her a glass of water. Her husband turned out to be a kind and compassionate man. He asked how long I would be hospitalised. I told him that was up to the Doctors. He invited me to stay with them on my leave for as long as I liked, a kind offer which I accepted.

One day, I had a surprise visit from the Captain of *The Usworth*. He had been informed by a friend at the Admiralty that the last crew member of *The Usworth* had been brought home on the *S.S. Empire Bowmam*, also the news that Bunts had died at Iceland.

'So I felt I had to come and see you before I sail next week. Now,

O'Dell,' continued the Captain, 'what are your plans? I have already spoken to the Doctor here and he assures me you will make a complete recovery as far as your legs are concerned and that if you keep those glasses on, you will gradually lose the brown film over your eyes.' He explained to the Captain how the ex- cook from the Home and her husband had offered him a home with them, but he hoped to be back to sea as soon as he was fit.

They had a long talk about the future, while the Matron and the nurses kept coming to see that his visitor was well supplied with tea and biscuits. It was not often they had a full blown Captain in the other ranks ward, especially one with a newly sewn on ribbon of D.S.C.

The upshot of the talks was that, if he survived the war, he would get in touch with the shipping company W.I.S.C. and the Captain would help to get him a job in W.I.S.C.

'From your eye trouble, it's obvious you cannot become a Deck Officer, and you have not served your time to become a ship's Engineer Officer but, if you really buckled down to it and studied accountancy, you could, after working your way through to a Catering Officer, eventually become a Chief Purser. Think about it, O'Dell. But remember I can only get you a start in the W.I.S.C., after that it's up to you how high you climb. Remember. in the W.I.S.C., a Chief Purser equates with the Captain and Chief Engineer Officer.'

Later on, he had a visit from Nobby Clark, who had been sent to join a ship in South Shields as one of the D.E.M.S. Gunners. Nobby was thrilled with his progress. 'You will be out in no time and back to sea. You have made a marvellous recovery.' Nobby also brought him his first bottle of 'Morgan Pomade' to dye his hair. 'The grey will soon disappear with 'Morgans' I promise you,' chuckled Nobby.

He was a good friend and he was very grateful to him for his visit. Who would have thought that day that Nobby was to die a few days after D-Day when the destroyer he was on, in company with another destroyer, was sunk by the R.A.F. A wartime accident and accepted as such; no one thought to gain or make waves in those days, even though seven officers and forty three crewmen died.

One day, the Matron told him he was to appear in front of a panel, consisting of three Doctors, to see if he could be judged fit enough to return to light duties. He assured them at the interview he was fit and the brown film over his eyes was already thinning out; that most of his wounds and burns had healed well and that he had no trouble walking.

The Doctors asked him if he understood that he would have no sexual feelings for a long time and that he would never, ever, have children. He explained that the Russian Doctor, with the ship's Captain, had already given him that bad news in Russia.

He sensed the Doctors felt sorry, but he assured them that, as long as he could walk and see, he was happy.

A few days later, he was taken to *H.M.S. Ganges,* a training school taken over by the Navy for H.O. personnel. He was given light duties in the galley. Two weeks later, he was discharged from the T124X and released back to the Merchant Navy.

He took a train from Norwich to Newcastle-upon-Tyne where he was met by the couple who had invited him to stay with them.

The village was not far from Newcastle and it was decided that they would call him 'Tom' and he would call them 'Aunty and Uncle'. As they were both in their fifties, and it being a first time marriage for both of them, they looked on him as someone who had made their family complete. Over the years, he was to grow to love them.

On joining the 'Shipping Pool' at Newcastle, and after undergoing a medical, he was surprised to find that he had to revert back to a mess boy as he was not 17 years old. He was also to find out, slowly but surely, that having left the Merchant Navy for the T124X, i.e. the Royal Navy, this fact was being held against him and that he was being passed over as jobs came, not once, but time and time again.

You must appreciate my wages had stopped once I was sunk going to Russia and, although I had received my wages due me before the sinking, plus my work on the *H.M.S. Ganges*, it did not amount to much and it was going fast. It's true one got £1. 2s. 0d. a week from the 'Pool' but you had to pay for your digs, bus fares, clothes etc., out of that. Aunty and Uncle, bless them, told me not to worry about paying for my keep until I had a job but I managed, under the 'shipwreck' scheme, to draw extra food and clothing coupons, which helped Aunty, but my pride demanded a job.

The day came when my luck changed. I had just left the 'Pool' and was passing the shipping office building, on my way to Bigg Lane to buy off ration rabbit stew, when I literally banged into a lady and

185

gentleman leaving the shipping office. As I turned to apologise, who should it be but the Captain of the Empire boat that had brought me home from Russia, the *Empire Bowman*.

For all my dyed hair, he recognised me right away. 'Well met, lad,' he said in his Scot accent, 'but that's my wife you're knocking about,' he added with a laugh. 'Gladys,' he said, 'this is the lad I told you about that we brought home in the Hospital.'

His wife was kindness itself and insisted on shaking hands. 'Why don't you join us,' asked the Captain. 'We are just going for a cup of tea at the Station Hotel.'

'Yes,' echoed his wife, 'do join us.'

So with thoughts of Bigg Market and rabbit stew firmly behind him, he had joined them for tea. After congratulating him on how fit he looked, the Captain asked what he was doing.

He found himself explaining how the T124X no longer required his service and how he seemed to be overlooked by the 'Pool' when jobs came in. 'The fact is, Captain, I am at my wits end and wondering whether to take a shore job to get some money.'

The Captain thought for a moment then a slow smile came over his face. Turning to his wife, who was still holding forth about how terrible it was that he should be treated like this, he said, 'Would you stay here, my dear, while I take this young lad with me to the shipping office.'

When we reached the shipping office the Captain said, 'Just sit on that bench lad, this may take some time.' After about twenty minutes, the Captain came out of a room and beckoned him over and asked him, 'Have you paid up your union dues, lad?' He assured the Captain he had. It was the first thing they had made him do at the 'Pool', pay his union dues up-to-date.

'Right,' replied the Captain. 'come in here.' On entering the room, a man sitting at a desk stood up. The Captain introduced him as the 'Shipping Master', another Scot, and a friend of the Captain's. Within five minutes, he had been signed on as Mess Steward for the *Empire Bowman*. On leaving, he tried to thank the Captain but he said, 'Don't give it another thought, lad. Just give me your word, and your hand, that you will never tell anyone on the ship. As far as they are concerned, the 'Pool' sent you.'

He gave his hand and his word and no one ever did find out the Captain's role.

He had joined the ship two days later. It was in Jarrow Dock having torpedo nets fitted. Apart from the Third Engineer Officer, Norman, the whole ship's complement had changed.

The first voyage on the *Empire Bowman* was to Gibralter, North Africa, then the landing of Canadian troops at Sicily. He had been frightened but he felt what he was doing was nothing to compare with what those gallant Canadian soldiers did as they left the ship's side, scrambling down the nets into the landing craft, then heading for the beach and coming under vicious small arms fire as it raked the beach; those Canadians sure had guts.

As they laid off Sicily that evening with about fourteen other ships, with a cruiser and destroyers for protection, they were attacked by U.S.A. Airforce bombers. It was unbelievable to watch the bombers, with their large white stars painted on their wings, coming at them. In the end, the Navy had to put up a low barrage. By the time the Americans got the message that they were attacking their allies, they had badly damaged two merchant ships, one of which had to be beached after most of its crew had been taken off. Another wartime genuine mistake and recognised as such but, of course, that did not stop the lads on the ship calling the Americans some pretty awful names, especially as a lot of the crew had been getting 'Dear Johns' from their wives and sweethearts and it always seemed to be an American making the triangle. They used to say 'those bastards are overpaid, oversexed and over here'. The 'Dear John' letters used to be posted on the notice board and the excuses the women used to come out with had to be seen to be believed.

After Sicily, the *Empire Bowman* was ordered to South Africa, via Suez, Red Sea, Aden, then Capetown. Somehow the *Empire Bowman*, although a happy ship, lacked the comradeship and closeness of the *Llandudno* and, of course, with its big fridges for food and cold air blowers in each cabin, no one felt the heat of the Red Sea except the firemen and Engineer Officers.

After dry-docking in Capetown, the ship was ordered to Vitoria, Brazil, where she loaded pig iron for America and, for nearly the whole of the rest of the war, the ship was on the South American coast running up to the United States or Canada; sometimes from Brazil to West Indies, then the West Indies to America with bauxite. Nearly everyone on the ship moaned but I enjoyed it to the full, resting, sunbathing and exercise soon got me back to full health. I had had enough of war. We were in Bahia, Brazil, on D-day. The Captain was furious, as were some of the crew, but I certainly was not.

I have to plead guilty to having enjoyed the last year of the war. I found the South American people so warm and kind, wonderful people.'

'Well,' said the lady reporter, 'thank you for the interesting story, there are three questions I would like to ask. First, did you ever see Yearly again?'

'Yes, but not until he was about 73 years old. I went to visit the Naval School after the war, they told me he had retired in 1944 but, years later, they dragged him out of retirement at one of our reunions. He looked so old and pitiful, walking with two sticks, that all my hatred died away.'

'Second. Is your sister still alive?'

'No. I received word from the War Office that she died in Egypt in a bomb attack by Italian Airforce while I was in Russia.'

'Third. Can you remember how you felt when you left the Tl 24X? Did you feel the Navy had used you? Did you feel at that time useless?'

'The answer is no. I never felt used or useless, but I will tell you something that did happen as I left the 'Ganges'. It was about 0900hrs. As I went to march out of the gate, one of the Military Police at the gate stopped me. He was one of those brutal types they had in those days, all brawn and nothing between the ears. He read the pass and discharge form, sneered, and said 'Another one who cannot take it.'

He had felt his temper rise, when a voice from the guard house shouted, 'If that is someone going to the station, I will give him a lift in the jeep in a few minutes.'

'No, it's all right,' the M.P. shouted back as he handed me my papers, 'this one is walking—besides, he is only a pisspot jerker.'

I felt a rush of blood but, keeping my tongue between my teeth I thought, stuff you, you're looking at someone who intends to end up a Chief Purser in W.I.C.S.

And I did!